S0-ARN-877

Common Core

Standards for Mathematical Content

Domain Geometry

Cluster Identify and describe shapes (squares, circles, triangles, rectangles, hexagons, cubes, cones, cylinders, and spheres).

Standards K.G.2, K.G.3

Standards for Mathematical Practice

☑ Make sense of problems and persevere in solving them.

☑ Reason abstractly and quantitatively.

☑ Construct viable arguments and critique the reasoning of others.

☑ Model with mathematics.

☑ Use appropriate tools strategically.

☑ Attend to precision.

☑ Look for and make use of structure.

☑ Look for and express regularity in repeated reasoning.

Identifying and Describing Shapes

Planning

Lessons

Review and Assessment

ISBN-13: 978-0-328-67336-0
ISBN-10: 0-328-67336-6

4 5 6 7 8 9 10 V003 15 14 13 12 11

BIG IDEA Geometric Figures Two- and three-dimensional objects with or without curved surfaces can be described, classified, and analyzed by their attributes. An object's location in space can be described quantitatively.

ESSENTIAL UNDERSTANDINGS

14-1   A rectangle has four sides and four corners.

14-2   A square has four sides and four corners. All the sides of a square are the same length.

14-3   A circle is round and does not have any corners.

14-4   All triangles have three sides but can have different configurations of sides and angles.

14-5   A hexagon is a shape with six sides and six corners.

14-6   Three-dimensional or solid figures have length, width, and height. Many everyday objects closely approximate standard geometric solids.

14-7   Flat surfaces of many solid figures have specific shapes.

BIG IDEA Practices, Processes, and Proficiencies Mathematics content and practices can be applied to solve problems.

ESSENTIAL UNDERSTANDING

14-8   Some problems can be solved by using objects to act out the actions in the problem.

Geometry

Shapes

Geometry, the study of shapes and spatial relationships, is important because it offers children opportunities to relate mathematics to the real world. Young children need opportunities to explore the geometric world in which they live, to make observations and construct relationships about shape and space, and to solve problems in a spatial context. As children develop geometric concepts and spatial sense, they will benefit from the use of models and diagrams to learn other mathematical concepts.

Ⓒ Mathematical Practices: Use Structure

Help reinforce the concept that shapes are all around us. Ask children to find shapes in the classroom and draw them. For example, the board is a rectangle, a bookshelf might be a square, the clock is a circle.

Shapes

Plane Shapes and Solid Shapes

Children begin their geometric understanding visually. At the visual level, children judge a plane shape by its appearance as a whole. They use nonverbal thinking as they focus on the total shape and not the relationships of the sides, angles, or faces. Geometric knowledge gained at the visual level is then extended to the descriptive level at which children begin to focus on the specific attributes of plane and solid shapes and learn the language important in describing shapes according to their attributes. Young children first encounter examples of two-dimensional shapes, or plane shapes, as parts of objects in the real world. At the visual level, children must ignore all the other attributes of the real objects to focus on the simple plane shapes of triangles, rectangles (including squares), and circles. Young children also learn about three-dimensional shapes, or solid shapes, from objects in the real world. They develop an understanding of solid shapes first at the visual level and then they learn to connect informal language to formal geometric vocabulary (e.g., ball and sphere).

Ⓒ Mathematical Practices: Attend to Precision

Reinforce the attribute of shape by drawing a triangle on the board. Ask a child to come to the board and copy the triangle making it different from the one drawn. The child could make the new triangle larger or smaller or a different color, but it must still be the same shape. Repeat with other triangles and other shapes of different sizes and colors.

Ⓒ Mathematical Practices: Use Structure

Help children conceptualize the difference between a square and a rectangle. Show children a square block and a rectangular block. Ask children to compare the two shapes and tell you what is the same and what is different about the two blocks. Lead them to the conclusion that the only difference between the shapes is in the varied length of the sides of the rectangular block.

For a complete list of *enVisionMATH* Professional Development resources in print, on DVD, and online, see the *Teacher's Program Overview*.

INTERVENTION

ELL

STRATEGY
Use Repetition

Considerations for ELL Children

Repeated oral language practice of the words related to shape names will help English learners remember and understand the distinctions.

- Draw a circle, a triangle, a square, and a rectangle on the board. Ask children to name each shape. Help children pronounce the words as needed. Give children paper and a crayon. Say the name of one of the shapes and have children draw that shape.

Special Needs

 RTI

Considerations for Special Needs Children

- Review with special needs children the words *square, rectangle, circle,* and *triangle* and the shapes represented by the words.

- Hold up a paper cut out representation of each shape and have children identify it.

- Draw a square, a rectangle, a circle, and a triangle in one row on the board. Make paper shapes, including several of different sizes and colors of each shape, and put them in a paper bag.

- Call on a child to pick a shape from the grab bag and identify it. Then have the child tape the shape to the board under the drawing of the same shape.

- Repeat with other children until all the shapes are taped to the board.

Below Level

RTI

Considerations for Below Level Children

- Review with children the shapes circle, rectangle, square, and triangle. Make a bulletin board of the shapes.

- Help the children observe shapes in the classroom. Point out plane shapes in the environment during the day; for example, the clock is a circle; the desk is a rectangle; the floor tile is square.

- Have children draw the shapes they observe and post them in the correct category on the bulletin board. Help children label their drawings as needed.

- As children observe the shapes around them, they can add to the bulletin board on a daily basis.

Advanced/Gifted

Considerations for Advanced/Gifted Children

- Children with a strong sense of shape will be able to identify figures that have the same shape *and* are the same size. Challenge them to identify pairs of such figures when they are not in the same relative position.

- Give children opportunities to connect geometry to concepts of comparison. Hold up a shape and have children find all the pattern blocks with *more* sides, *fewer* sides, or the *same* number of sides.

Response to Intervention

 RTI
TIER **1** ONGOING

Ongoing Intervention
- Lessons with guiding questions to assess understanding
- Support to prevent misconceptions and to reteach

 RTI
TIER **2** STRATEGIC

Strategic Intervention
- Targeted to small groups who need more support
- Easy to implement

 RTI
TIER **3** INTENSIVE

Intensive Intervention
- Instruction to accelerate progress
- Instruction focused on foundational skills

MATHEMATICAL
PRACTICES

Reading Comprehension and Problem Solving

@ Use Structure:
Using Reading Comprehension Strategies
Even when math problems are presented using a picture book format, a good reading comprehension strategy to use in math problem-solving is to describe objects.

Questions to Guide Comprehension
Use these comprehension questions with Exercise 1 in Lesson 14-8. *What do you need to find out?* [Which shape matches the shape of the kite?] *What do you know?* [The kite has 4 sides and 4 corners.]

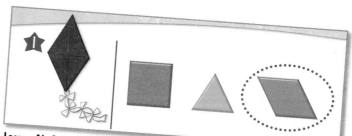

Lesson 14-8, Exercise 1

Act It Out! *How can you use pattern blocks to solve the problem?* Give each child one pattern block of each shape. Have children manipulate the pattern blocks and place each one on the corresponding picture to determine which shape matches the shape of the kite.

Talk It Out! *How can you tell a story about the shapes to solve the problem?* Help children describe the characteristics of the shapes to find out which one matches the shape of the kite. *The kite has 4 corners and 4 sides. Which shape has 4 corners and 4 sides?* [Square, blue shape] *Some of the kite's sides are slanted. Which of the 2 shapes has slanted sides?* [Blue shape]

Draw It Out! *How can you draw a picture to solve the problem?* Give each child one pattern block of each shape. Children can trace the outline of each shape on a sheet of paper. Have children compare the outlines to one another, and then compare each outline to the shape of the kite to find which outline matches its shape.

Vocabulary Activities

Word Web
@ **Attend to Precision** Use the vocabulary graphic organizer Word Web (Teaching Tool 17). Make one copy of the teaching tool and write the word "square" and draw a simple square in the center oval. Then make copies so that every child has his or her own page. Have children write words or draw a picture at the end of each line to help them remember the word's meaning. For example, children can write "4 corners" or draw a square window or a square house.

As you progress through the topic and children learn different two-dimensional shapes, have them use the vocabulary model to show each of the words in a variety of ways.

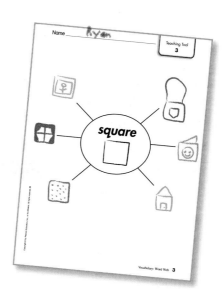

Social Studies Center

Along the Way

Materials
Chart paper, crayons, cardboard shapes to match pictures

- Draw a picture of a stop sign on chart paper. Also, draw a one-way sign, a speed-limit sign, and a school sign.

- Provide partners with cardboard shapes that match the shapes of the traffic signs. Then have children take turns counting the number of sides of each shape.

- Partners can trace the cardboard shapes that have the same shapes as traffic signs and draw inside the outlines to make each sign.

Movement Center

Act It Out!

Materials
Attribute blocks (or Teaching Tool 36), paper bag

- Place the attribute blocks in the bag. Have children choose the blocks one-at-a-time and identify the shape.

- Ask them to model the shape using their hands or working with other children to form the shape with their bodies.

- Ask children to describe the shape they formed using the words *side* and *corner*.

Math Center

Puzzle Shapes

Materials
Various large cardboard shapes, blunt-tipped scissors

- Have children make puzzle pieces from cardboard shapes by drawing lines on the cardboard shapes and then cutting the pieces out.

- Once they have cut the puzzle pieces, have them complete the puzzle and describe the shape.

- Children can switch puzzles with a partner.

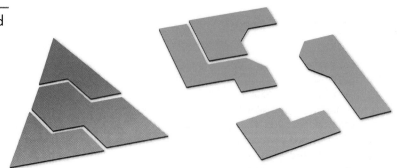

Dramatic Play Center

Cookie Fun

Materials
Clay, glitter, plastic knives or cookie cutters in various shapes

- Have children use clay to bake "cookies" in different shapes—circles, squares, triangles, and rectangles.
- Then have children act out a party scene.

Art Center

Shaping Up

Materials
Colored yarn, dark construction paper, glue, blunt-tipped scissors

- Have children make a yarn collage of different shapes. They might overlap 2 circles or squares or add rectangles and triangles to the picture.
- Some children might make a simple animal with the yarn shapes.
- Then have children describe the shapes in their designs using the words *side* and *corner*.

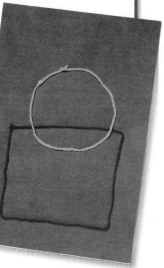

Building Center

Animal Shapes

Materials
Pattern Blocks (or Teaching Tool 35)

- Have children use pattern blocks to build animals.
- Have them present what they have built, describing the shapes they used to build their animals.

Identifying and Describing Shapes
INTERACTIVE MATH STORY

On My Way to School

This is a story in which children identify some two-dimensional shapes.

1 ▶ Before the Story

Picture Walk

Hold up the big book and read the title, author's name, and illustrator's name to children. Ask children to look at the pages. *Where does the story take place?* [At home, the yard, around town, at school] *Who are the main characters?* [A boy and his mom] *What do you think the story is about?* [What the boy and his mom do on the way to school]

Activate Prior Knowledge

In this story, we identify some two-dimensional shapes. Point to the clock and the door in the classroom. *How are these shapes different from one another?* [One is round; it is a circle; one is a rectangle. One has corners; the other is smooth all the way around.]

This book belongs to:

Jessie

Topic 14 Story

On My Way to School
Written by Kerry Childers and Gretchen Seidel
Illustrated by Paul Sharp

It's time for school! Hurry, hurry across the floor, down the hall and out the door. The is a ◯◻.

Topic 14   **1**

Hurry, hurry through the yard. Spotting shapes isn't hard. The ▱ on the house is a △ .

Topic 14   **2**

2 ▶ During the Story

READ

Read the story aloud for enjoyment. Explain that there are shapes in the pictures. Page 1: *What shape is the door?* [Rectangle] Direct children's attention to the other shapes on the page. *What other shapes do you see?* [Square, circle] Continue in this manner.

GESTURE

Have children point to specific shapes on each page. On page 1 point out that the wheels, the mirror, and the doorknob are shaped like circles. Have children point to something in the classroom that is shaped like a circle. Refer to page 3 and have children point to 2 triangles. Finally, on page 4, have children point to 3 rectangles.

hurry, hurry through the ~~to~~wn. I see shapes both ~~u~~p and down. The 🕐 is ⭕ ⬜.

Topic 14 **3**

The trip to school takes awhile, but finding shapes makes me smile. The ⬡ **has a** ⬣ ⬜ **in it.**

Topic 14 **4**

fold down

3 > ## After the Story

Extension

Play a guessing game with children. For example: *I see something in the classroom that is a rectangle. You sit on it during storytime. What is it?* [Rug] Then call on a volunteer to do the same. Have him or her select an object and give clues describing it. If needed, prompt the child with descriptions by whispering in his or her ear.

You may wish to have children take home their Interactive Math Story books and share what they have learned about two-dimensional shapes.

COLOR

Distribute the Interactive Math Story books to children. Read the story aloud page by page. Then direct children to color on each page. Page 1: Color the door blue. Page 2: Color the roof of the house orange. Page 3: Color the clock purple. Page 4: Color the hexagon in the jungle gym green.

WRITE

Reread the story to children. This time have them circle the answers to the questions raised in the text. Page 1: the rectangle; page 2: the trapezoid; page 3: the circle, and page 4: the hexagon.

SPEAK

Invite children to retell the story in their own words. Encourage them to say the names of the shapes they recognize. Prompt them with questions. *What shape is the door?* [Rectangle] *The clock?* [Circle] *The top of the jungle gym?* [Hexagon]

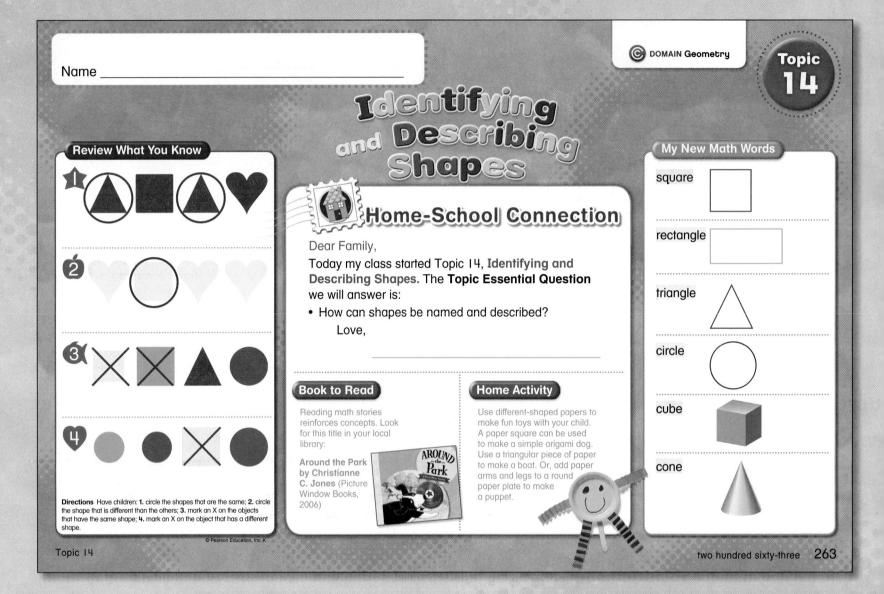

Review What You Know

Purpose

Diagnose children's readiness by assessing prerequisite content. Then use the Intervention System if needed.

Understanding by Design

Children will be able to answer the Topic Essential Question by the end of the topic. Revisit the question throughout the topic. Then use the Topic 14 Performance Assessment.

Topic Essential Question

• How can shapes be named and described?

"Understanding by Design" is registered as a trademark with the Patent and Trademark Office by the Association for Supervision of Curriculum Development (ASCD). ASCD has not authorized, approved or sponsored this work and is in no way affiliated with Pearson or its products.

rectangle

Cards can always be used as flash cards. Have children create large vocabulary cards with visuals to add to the classroom word wall.

Shapeland Dog Park

What You Need

2 counters ● ○
paper clip
pencil

Number of Players: 2

How to Play

1. Place your counter on START.
2. Take turns. Spin the spinner.
3. Move your counter to the shape you spin.
4. Play until you reach a red shape.

Topic 14

two hundred sixty-four 264

Game
for school or home

Purpose

Provide children with an opportunity to practice prerequisite skills. Before they begin the game, you may wish to review with children the concepts of same and different.

Math Project

Art

Directions

Have children find different shapes in the classroom, including circles, squares, rectangles, and triangles. Have children draw each object on a separate sheet of construction paper. Have them name each shape and then help them label the shapes. Publish children's pictures in a class book.

Rectangle

Domain

Geometry

Cluster

Identify and describe shapes (squares, circles, triangles, rectangles, hexagons, cubes, cones, cylinders, and spheres).

Standard

K.G.2 Correctly name shapes regardless of their orientations or overall size.

Mathematical Practices

○ Make sense of problems and persevere in solving them.

✔ Reason abstractly and quantitatively.

✔ Construct viable arguments and critique the reasoning of others.

○ Model with mathematics.

✔ Use appropriate tools strategically.

✔ Attend to precision.

✔ Look for and make use of structure.

○ Look for and express regularity in repeated reasoning.

Rectangles

 Lesson Overview

Objective	Essential Understanding	Vocabulary	Materials
Children will identify and describe rectangles.	A rectangle has four sides and four corners.	**rectangle** **side** **corner**	Rectangle attribute blocks (Teaching Tool 36), Rectangles (Teaching Tool 19), blunt-tipped scissors, glue

© **PROFESSIONAL DEVELOPMENT**

Math Background

A rectangle is a quadrilateral with 4 right angles. Notice that this does not say anything about the length of the sides. If 2 of the sides are one length and the other 2 sides are a different length, we think of this shape as a rectangle.

If all of the sides are the same length, it is still a rectangle because there are 4 right angles and 4 sides. A square is a special type of rectangle that children will learn about in the next lesson.

1 Daily Common Core Review

Daily Common Core Review

Name _____

Daily Common Core Review **14-1**

❶ 🌿🌿🌿🌿🌿🌿🌿   🌿🌿

Ⓐ 10

Ⓑ 9

Ⓒ 8

Ⓓ 7

❷

Ⓐ 3 + 2 = 5

Ⓑ 3 + 3 = 6

Ⓒ 3 + 0 = 3

Ⓓ 2 + 2 = 4

Content Reviewed

Exercise 1   Use Numbers to Tell How Many

Exercise 2   Solve Joining Stories

Also available in print

Problem-Based Interactive Learning

30 min

Overview Children will identify shapes that are rectangles.

Focus How can you tell if a shape is a rectangle?

Materials (per child) Rectangle attribute blocks (Teaching Tool 36), Rectangles (Teaching Tool 19), blunt-tipped scissors, glue

Vocabulary rectangle, side, corner

Set the Purpose Remind children that objects can be sorted by shape. *You will learn about a shape called a rectangle in this lesson.*

Connect Hold up 4 fingers. *How many fingers am I holding up?* [4]

MATHEMATICAL **PRACTICES**

Use Structure
Remind children that they can determine if a shape is a rectangle by looking at the shape's attributes. Discuss the attributes of rectangles, emphasizing the words *side* and *corner* as important vocabulary.

Academic Vocabulary Distribute a **rectangle** attribute block to each child or pairs of children. Hold up a block as you describe it. *This shape is a rectangle. A rectangle has 4 sides and 4 corners.* Point to one set of the straight (parallel) sides and have children finger-trace the sides. *These sides are the same length.* Point to the second set of straight (parallel) sides. *These sides are the same length.* Have children finger-trace the second set of parallel sides. *Can you find anything in the classroom that has a shape like a rectangle?* [Possible responses: table, bulletin board, book]

Pose the Problem *Lin's mother is buying a shade for a window in Lin's room.* Draw a rectangular window on the chalkboard. *How will she figure out the shape of the window?* Have children share their ideas for solving the problem before you model a possible solution.

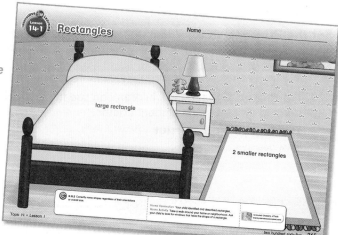

Model Have children cut out the shapes from Teaching Tool 19 or distribute the shapes to them. Hold up the large rectangular paper shape and have children do the same. *Is this a rectangle?* [Yes] *How many sides does a rectangle have?* [4] *Are all of the sides the same length?* [No] *How many corners does it have?* [4] Point to the opposite sides. *These opposite sides are the same length.* Point to the other opposite sides. *These opposite sides are the same length.* Place the large rectangle on the left side of the workmat. *Find the large rectangle. How do you know it is a rectangle?* [It has 4 sides and 4 corners.] Then have them glue it onto the left side of the workmat. Hold up one of the smaller rectangles horizontally and then vertically. Discuss why the shape is also a rectangle. Have children glue the two smaller rectangles onto the right side of the workmat.

Use Gestures and Facial Expressions Use a variety of gestures and facial expressions while you are talking to get and keep children's attention and to emphasize key concepts.

Put 2 rectangles together to make a larger rectangle. Give children 2 rectangle attribute blocks and have them find a solution.

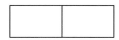

eTools **Geometry Shapes**
www.pearsonsuccessnet.com

What shape was traced? How do you know? [Rectangle; it has 4 sides and 4 corners. The opposite sides are the same size.]

What do you see? [A person holding a dollar bill] *What shape is the dollar bill?* [Rectangle] *How do you know?* [It has 4 sides and 4 corners. The opposite sides are the same size.]

1 Visual Learning

Set the Purpose Call children's attention to the **Visual Learning Bridge** at the top of the page. *In this lesson, you will learn about rectangles.*

 Animated Glossary Children can see highlighted words defined in the Online Student Edition.

rectangle, **side**, **corner**

www.pearsonsuccessnet.com

2 Guided Practice

Remind children that rectangles can be different sizes.

Error Intervention

If children have difficulty identifying a rectangle because of different sizes or widths,

then review the attributes of a rectangle.

Do you understand? Draw a circle, a triangle, and a rectangle on the board. *Which shape is a rectangle? How do you know?* [The rectangle has 4 sides and 4 corners. The opposite sides are the same size.]

Reteaching Trace paper rectangles of different sizes onto cardboard to make templates. Have children choose 2 rectangles to trace onto construction paper. Have them cut out their rectangles. Discuss with children what makes a shape a rectangle.

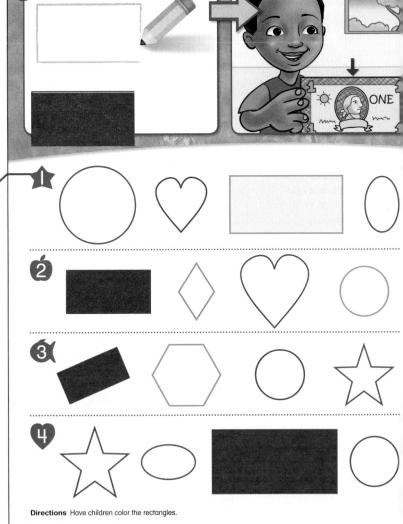

Directions Have children color the rectangles.

Topic 14 • Lesson 1

What do you see? [A person holding an envelope] *What shape is the envelope?* [Rectangle] *How many sides does it have?* [4] *How many corners does it have?* [4]

What shape is the side of the box? [Rectangle] *What other objects might have this shape?* [Answers will vary.]

Directions Have children circle the objects that are shaped like a rectangle.

two hundred sixty-six 266

Additional Activity

Clay Shapes

⏱ 10 min 👥

Materials Clay, attribute blocks: circles, triangles, rectangles

- Have children flatten the clay and then press one attribute block into the clay to make an imprint. *Is the shape a rectangle? How do you know?*
- Have children choose another attribute block and repeat the activity.

3 **Independent Practice**

Children circle objects that are shaped like a rectangle.

266A

Close

Essential Understanding A rectangle has four sides and four corners.
A rectangle has opposite sides that are the same length. It has four corners that are all the same size. Remember that rectangles can be different sizes.

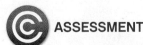 **ASSESSMENT**

Exercise 1 is worth 1 point.
Use the rubric to score Exercise 2.

Exercise 2
Use Structure Children should be able to color pictures to identify objects shaped like rectangles.

E L L Rephrase For children who need additional help, rephrase the key words as you describe a rectangle.

Student Samples
3-point answer Children color 3 objects with a rectangular shape and describe the shape of a rectangle. A child might say, "A rectangle has 4 sides and 4 corners. The opposite sides are the same length."

2-point answer Children color 2 objects with the shape of a rectangle.

1-point answer Children color an incorrect object.

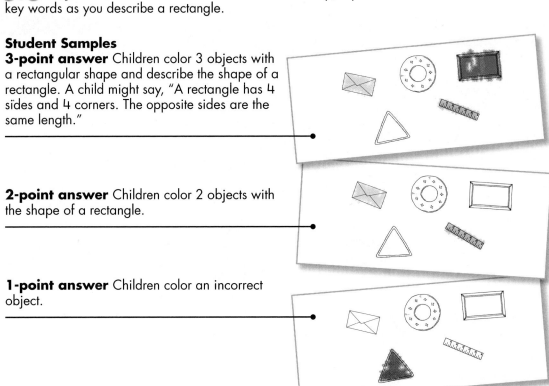

Quick Check Master

Name _____

Quick Check
14-1

⬆ ● ☐

Ⓑ ◯

Ⓒ △

Ⓓ ⬡

❷

See student samples at the right.

Directions Have children: ⬆ fill in the bubble next to the rectangle; ❷ color the objects that are shaped like a rectangle and then describe the shape of a rectangle.

 **Formative** Assessment

Use the **Quick Check** to assess children's understanding.

Prescription for Differentiated Instruction

Use children's work on the **Quick Check** to prescribe differentiated instruction.

Points	Prescription
0–2	Intervention
3	On-Level
4	Advanced

Differentiated Instruction

Intervention

Sponge Designs

 10 min

Materials (per group) Sponges cut into different sizes of rectangles, paint, construction paper

- Have children dip a sponge into a tray of paint and gently press it onto the paper to print the shape. *What is the shape you made?* [Rectangle]

- Have children choose different-sized rectangular sponges to press onto their paper to make a design.

- Ask children to describe the shape of the rectangle in their finished pictures.

On-Level

Practice | Center Activity

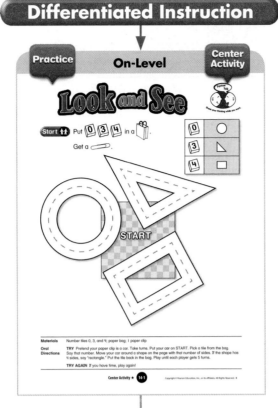

Materials Number tiles 0, 3, and 4; paper bag; 1 paper clip
Oral Directions **TRY** Pretend your paper clip is a car. Take turns. Put your car on START. Pick a tile from the bag. Say that number. Move your car around a shape on the page with that number of sides. If the shape has 4 sides, say "rectangle." Put the tile back in the bag. Play until each player gets 5 turns.
TRY AGAIN If you have time, play again!

Center Activity ★ 14-1

Advanced

Practice | Center Activity

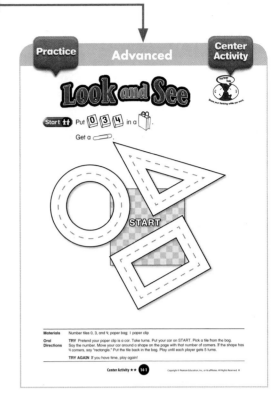

Materials Number tiles 0, 3, and 4; paper bag; 1 paper clip
Oral Directions **TRY** Pretend your paper clip is a car. Take turns. Put your car on START. Pick a tile from the bag. Say the number. Move your car around a shape on the page with that number of corners. If the shape has 4 corners, say "rectangle." Put the tile back in the bag. Play until each player gets 5 turns.
TRY AGAIN If you have time, play again!

Center Activity ★★ 14-1

ELL Partner Talk Listen for the word *rectangle*. For example, a child might say, "I picked 4. A *rectangle* has 4 sides. I can move my car around a *rectangle*."

Leveled Homework

Reteaching Master

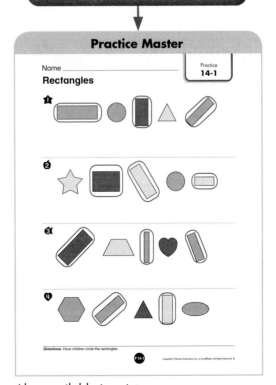

Name _____
Rectangles

Reteaching 14-1

Check children's tracings to make sure they understand what a rectangle is.

Directions Have children: ★ describe the rectangle street sign and trace the shape next to it to complete the rectangle sign; ❷ trace the rectangle to make a chimney and then trace the other rectangles in the picture.

Also available in print

Practice Master

Name _____
Rectangles

Practice 14-1

Directions Have children circle the rectangles.

Also available in print

Enrichment Master

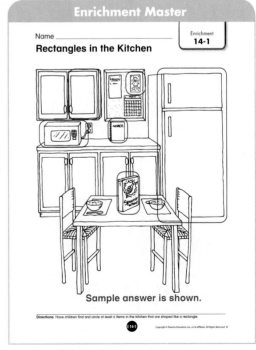

Name _____
Rectangles in the Kitchen

Enrichment 14-1

Sample answer is shown.

Directions Have children find and circle at least 6 items in the kitchen that are shaped like a rectangle.

Also available in print

Domain

Geometry

Cluster

Identify and describe shapes (squares, circles, triangles, rectangles, hexagons, cubes, cones, cylinders, and spheres).

Standard

K.G.2 Correctly name shapes regardless of their orientations or overall size.

Mathematical Practices

○ Make sense of problems and persevere in solving them.

○ Reason abstractly and quantitatively.

☑ Construct viable arguments and critique the reasoning of others.

○ Model with mathematics.

☑ Use appropriate tools strategically.

☑ Attend to precision.

☑ Look for and make use of structure.

○ Look for and express regularity in repeated reasoning.

Squares

 **Lesson Overview**

Objective	Essential Understanding	Vocabulary	Materials
Children will identify and describe squares.	A square has four sides and four corners. All the sides of a square are the same length.	**square**	Square attribute blocks (Teaching Tool 36), Squares (Teaching Tool 20), blunt-tipped scissors, glue

Ⓒ PROFESSIONAL DEVELOPMENT

Math Background

Research says . . . kindergarten children will soon be making a transition from identifying a square as a square "just because it looks like one," and identifying it as a square because it has the properties of a square: 4 sides, equal sides, 4 square corners. They will also make a similar transition with other simple geometric shapes (van Hiele, 1986).

1 Daily Common Core Review

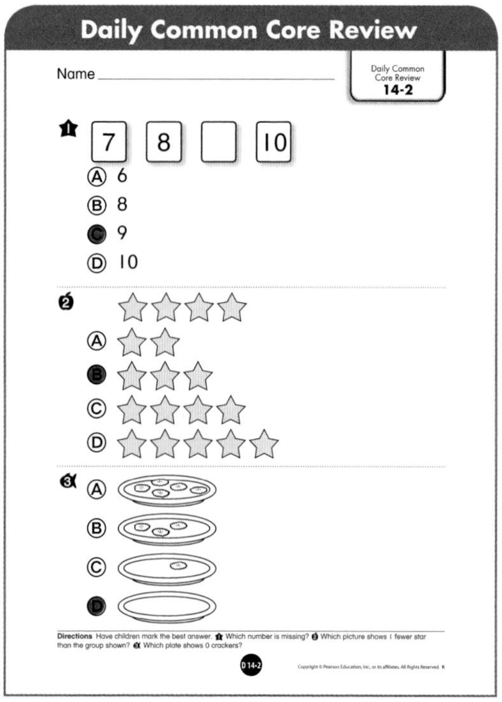

Daily Common Core Review

Name _____

Daily Common Core Review **14-2**

❶ [7] [8] [ ] [10]

Ⓐ 6

Ⓑ 8

⬤ 9

Ⓓ 10

❷ ☆☆☆☆

Ⓐ ☆☆

⬤ ☆☆☆

Ⓒ ☆☆☆☆

Ⓓ ☆☆☆☆☆

❸ Ⓐ 🍪🍪🍪🍪

Ⓑ 🍪🍪🍪

Ⓒ 🍪

⬤ (empty plate)

Directions Have children mark the best answer. ❶ Which number is missing? ❷ Which picture shows 1 fewer star than the group shown? ❸ Which plate shows 0 crackers?

Also available in print

Content Reviewed

Exercise 1   Order Numbers to 10

Exercise 2   Identify 1 Fewer

Exercise 3   Count Objects

 MATHEMATICAL PRACTICES

 30 min **Problem-Based Interactive Learning**

Overview Children will identify shapes that are squares.

Focus How can you tell if a shape is a square?

Materials (per child) Square attribute blocks (Teaching Tool 36), Squares (Teaching Tool 20), blunt-tipped scissors, glue

Vocabulary square

Set the Purpose Remind children that they have learned about rectangles. *You will learn about a shape called a square in this lesson.*

Connect Draw a rectangle on the board. *Is this a rectangle?* [Yes] *How do you know?* [It has 4 sides and 4 corners. Its opposite sides are the same length.]

MATHEMATICAL PRACTICES

Use Appropriate Tools Emphasize the importance of attribute blocks as appropriate tools to think about the similarities and differences between rectangles and squares.

Academic Vocabulary Distribute a **square** attribute block to each child or pairs of children. Hold up a block as you describe it. *This shape is a square. A square has 4 sides and 4 corners.* Point to each of the sides and have children finger-trace the sides. *All of these sides are the same length. Can you find anything in the classroom that has a shape like a square?* [Possible responses: window, picture frame]

Pose the Problem *John wants to find square toys in his yard. How can he figure out which toys are square?* Have children share their ideas before you model a possible solution.

Model Have children cut out the shapes from Teaching Tool 20 or distribute the shapes to them. Hold up the large square paper shape and have children do the same. *Is this a square?* [Yes] *How many sides does a square have?* [4] *Are all of the sides the same length?* [Yes] *How many corners does it have?* [4] *Are all of the corners the same?* [Yes] Place the large square on the left side of the workmat. *Find the large square. How do you know it is a rectangle?* [It has 4 sides and 4 corners.] Then have them glue it onto the left side of the workmat. Hold up one of the smaller squares. Discuss why the shape is also a square. Have children glue the two smaller squares onto the right side of the workmat. *These are shapes that John wants to play with in the pool and in the sandbox.* Explain that a square is a special kind of rectangle because the sides are all the same length. Draw a square and a rectangle on the board. *How are these shapes alike?* [They both have 4 sides and 4 corners.] *How are they different?* [The square has 4 sides that are the same length.]

Use Gestures and Facial Expressions Use a variety of gestures and facial expressions while you are talking to get and keep children's attention and to emphasize key concepts.

 Put 4 squares together to make a larger square. Give children 4 square attribute blocks of the same size and have them find a solution.

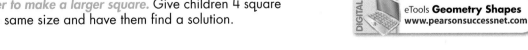

eTools **Geometry Shapes**
www.pearsonsuccessnet.com

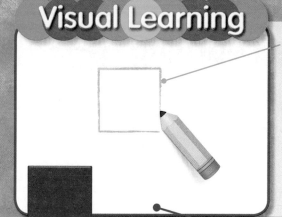

Visual Learning

What shape is being traced? [Square] *How do you know?* [It has 4 sides and 4 corners. The 4 sides are the same.]

What do you see? [A person holding a cracker] *What shape is the cracker?* [Square] *How do you know?* [It has 4 sides and 4 corners. The 4 sides are the same. The 4 corners are the same size.]

1 Visual Learning

Set the Purpose Call children's attention to the **Visual Learning Bridge** at the top of the page. *In this lesson, you will learn about squares.*

 Animated Glossary Children can see highlighted words defined in the Online Student Edition.

square

www.pearsonsuccessnet.com

2 Guided Practice

Remind children that squares can be different sizes.

Error Intervention

If children confuse squares and rectangles,

then place a square next to a rectangle. Talk about each shape and its attributes.

Do you understand? *What does a square look like?* [It has 4 sides that are the same length and 4 corners that are the same size.]

Reteaching Trace paper squares of different sizes onto cardboard to make templates. Have children choose 2 squares to trace onto construction paper. Have them cut out their squares. Discuss what makes a shape a square with children.

Directions Have children color the squares.

Topic 14 • Lesson 2

What shape is the clock? [Square] *How many corners does it have?* [4]

What do you see? [A picture in a frame] *What shape is the frame?* [Square] *Is it a rectangle?* [Yes. A square is a special kind of rectangle.] *What is special about a square?* [All the sides are the same length.]

Directions Have children circle the objects that are shaped like a square.

two hundred sixty-eight **268**

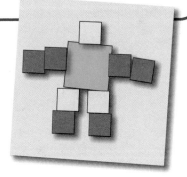
3 Independent Practice

Children circle objects that are shaped like a square.

268A

Close

Essential Understanding A square has four equal sides and four corners. All the sides of a square are the same length. *A square has four sides that are the same length and four corners. Remember that rectangles have opposite sides that are the same length, but squares have all four sides that are the same length.*

Quick Check Master

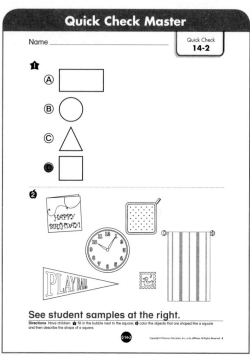

Name _____

Quick Check
14-2

Ⓐ ▭

Ⓑ ◯

Ⓒ △

Ⓓ ▢

See student samples at the right.

Directions Have children: ★ fill in the bubble next to the square; ② color the objects that are shaped like a square and then describe the shape of a square.

Copyright © Pearson Education, Inc., or its affiliates. All Rights Reserved. K

Formative Assessment

Use the **Quick Check** to assess children's understanding.

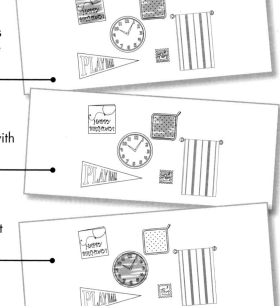

© **ASSESSMENT**

Exercise 1 is worth 1 point.
Use the rubric to score Exercise 2.

Exercise 2
Use Structure Children should be able to color pictures to identify objects shaped like squares.

E L L Rephrase For children who need additional help, rephrase keywords as you describe a square.

Student Samples
3-point answer Children color 3 objects with a square shape and describe the shape of a square. A child might say, "A square has 4 sides and 4 corners. All of the sides are the same size."

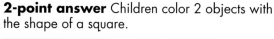

2-point answer Children color 2 objects with the shape of a square.

1-point answer Children color an incorrect object.

Prescription for Differentiated Instruction
Use children's work on the **Quick Check** to prescribe differentiated instruction.

Points	Prescription
0–2	Intervention
3	On-Level
4	Advanced

Differentiated Instruction

Intervention

Measuring Squares and Rectangles

 10 min

Materials (per pair) 4½" posterboard squares, 1½" × 3" posterboard rectangles, connecting cubes

- Model using connecting cubes to measure the sides of posterboard shapes. Measure a square and demonstrate that all sides are the same length. *Each side of this square is the same size as 6 cubes. All the sides of the square are the same length.*

- Measure a rectangle showing that only the opposite sides are the same length.

- Have partners measure the sides of the posterboard shapes and explain which ones are squares and which ones are rectangles.

On-Level
Practice · **Center Activity**

Start ↑↑ Put 1 2 3 4 in a 📖.

Get 6 red squares.
Get 6 blue squares.

To win, get: ■■■ or ■ or ■ ■

Materials Number tiles 1–4, paper bag, 6 red squares, 6 blue squares

Oral Directions **TRY** Give 6 red squares to one player. Give 6 blue squares to the other player. Take turns. Pick a tile from the bag. Say the number. Tell about the shape next to that number. Find that shape on the game board. Trace that shape with your finger. Cover it with a square. If the shape is a square, say "square," and tell why that shape is a square. Put the tile back in the bag. You win if you get 3 squares that look like the ones below the game board.

TRY AGAIN If you have time, play again!

Center Activity ★ 14-2   Copyright © Pearson Education, Inc., or its affiliates. All Rights Reserved. K

Advanced
Practice · **Center Activity**

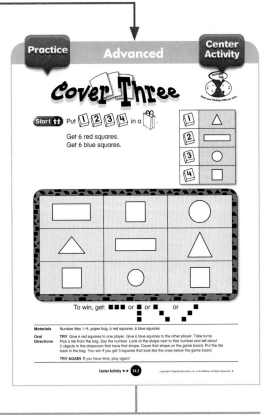

Start ↑↑ Put 1 2 3 4 in a 📖.

Get 6 red squares.
Get 6 blue squares.

To win, get: ■■■ or ■ or ■ ■

Materials Number tiles 1–4, paper bag, 6 red squares, 6 blue squares

Oral Directions **TRY** Give 6 red squares to one player. Give 6 blue squares to the other player. Take turns. Pick a tile from the bag. Say the number. Look at the shape next to that number and tell about 2 objects in the classroom that have that shape. Cover that shape on the game board. Put the tile back in the bag. You win if you get 3 squares that look like the ones below the game board.

TRY AGAIN If you have time, play again!

Center Activity ★★ 14-2   Copyright © Pearson Education, Inc., or its affiliates. All Rights Reserved. K

ELL **Report Back** To check understanding, ask a child to repeat and complete this sentence: *A square has 4 straight sides that have the same_____.* [Size]

Leveled Homework

Reteaching Master

Name_____ Reteaching **14-2**

Squares

Directions Have children: ★ describe the square sign and trace the sign next to it to complete the square signs; ② circle the signs that are shaped like a square.

E14-2   Copyright © Pearson Education, Inc., or its affiliates. All Rights Reserved. K

Also available in print

Practice Master

Name_____ Practice **14-2**

Squares

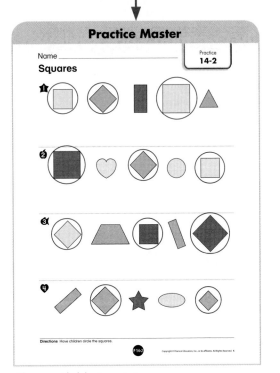

Directions Have children circle the squares.

P14-2   Copyright © Pearson Education, Inc., or its affiliates. All Rights Reserved. K

Also available in print

Enrichment Master

Name_____ Enrichment **14-2**

Connect the Dots to the Squares

Check children's work for accuracy. They should be able to recognize at least 5 squares in the picture.

Directions Have children connect the dots in order from 1 to 20 to complete the picture. Then have them use crayons to color in all the squares in the picture.

E14-2   Copyright © Pearson Education, Inc., or its affiliates. All Rights Reserved. K

Also available in print

DIGITAL eTools **Geometry Shapes**
www.pearsonsuccessnet.com

DIGITAL eTools **Geometry Shapes**
www.pearsonsuccessnet.com

DIGITAL eTools **Geometry Drawing**
www.pearsonsuccessnet.com

Common Core

Domain
Geometry

Cluster
Identify and describe shapes (squares, circles, triangles, rectangles, hexagons, cubes, cones, cylinders, and spheres).

Standard
K.G.2 Correctly name shapes regardless of their orientations or overall size.

Mathematical Practices
○ Make sense of problems and persevere in solving them.

○ Reason abstractly and quantitatively.

☑ Construct viable arguments and critique the reasoning of others.

○ Model with mathematics.

☑ Use appropriate tools strategically.

☑ Attend to precision.

☑ Look for and make use of structure.

○ Look for and express regularity in repeated reasoning.

Circles

 **Lesson Overview**

Objective	Essential Understanding	Vocabulary	Materials
Children will identify and describe circles.	A circle is round and does not have any corners.	**circle**	Circle attribute blocks (Teaching Tool 36), Circles (Teaching Tool 21), blunt-tipped scissors, glue

PROFESSIONAL DEVELOPMENT

Math Background

The classroom provides a wide variety of real objects that can be used to introduce and develop spatial sense. Call attention to the shapes of things used throughout children's daily activities, such as a rectangular sheet of paper or the circle formed by players in a game. Designate a "circle" day for children and look for objects shaped like a circle as they take a walk through the school or outside.

1 Daily Common Core Review

Content Reviewed

Exercise 1   Identify Ordinal Positions

Exercise 2   Use Numbers to Tell How Many

Also available in print

 30 min # Problem-Based Interactive Learning

Overview Children will identify shapes that are circles.

Focus How can you tell if a shape is a circle?

Materials (per child) Circle attribute block (Teaching Tool 36), Circles (Teaching Tool 21), blunt-tipped scissors, glue

Vocabulary circle

Set the Purpose Remind children that they have learned about rectangles and squares. *You will learn about a shape called a circle in this lesson.*

Connect Draw a square on the board. *Is this a square?* [Yes] *How do you know?* [It has 4 sides and 4 corners. All of its sides are the same length.]

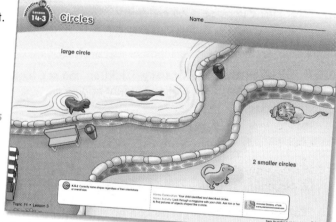

MATHEMATICAL PRACTICES

Use Structure
Help children understand that all circles are round and have no sides or corners, regardless of their size.

Academic Vocabulary Distribute a **circle** attribute block to each child or pairs of children. Hold up a block as you describe it. *This shape is a circle. A circle is round and has no corners.* Have children finger-trace around the circle. *Can you find anything in the classroom that has a shape like a circle?* [Possible response: clock]

Pose the Problem *The animals in the zoo like to play with toys that are shaped like circles. How can we figure out which toys are shaped like circles?* Have children share their ideas before you model a possible solution.

Model Have children cut out the shapes from Teaching Tool 21 or distribute the shapes to them. Hold up the large circular paper shape and have children do the same. *Is this a circle?* [Yes] *Does it have any sides?* [No] *Does it have any corners?* [No] *How else can you describe this shape?* [It is round.] Place the large circle on the left side of the workmat. *Find the large circle. How do you know it is a circle?* [It does not have any sides.] Then have them glue it onto the left side of the workmat. Hold up one of the smaller circles. Discuss why the shape is also a circle. Have children glue the two smaller circles onto the right side of the workmat. *These are the shapes of the toys that the animals like to play with in the zoo.*

Use Intonation Help children focus on the key vocabulary and key concepts by slightly exaggerating your intonation as you speak.

Small Group Interaction Have partners work together to review square, rectangle, and circle by drawing each shape. Ask children to identify each shape and tell about its attributes.

Draw an oval on the board. *Is this shape a circle? Why or why not?* [No, it isn't completely round.]

Visual Learning

What shape do you see? [Circle] *How do you know?* [It has no corners. It is round.]

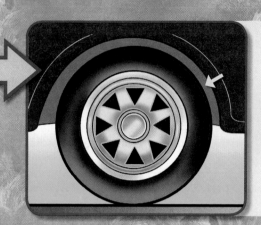

What do you see? [A tire] *What shape is the tire/wheel?* [Round; it is shaped like a circle.] *How are a circle and a rectangle different?* [A circle is round, and a rectangle has 4 corners.]

1 Visual Learning

Set the Purpose Call children's attention to the **Visual Learning Bridge** at the top of the page. *In this lesson, you will learn about circles.*

 Animated Glossary Children can see highlighted words defined in the Online Student Edition.

circle

www.pearsonsuccessnet.com

2 Guided Practice

Remind children that circles can be different sizes.

Error Intervention

If children confuse circles and ovals,

then place a paper circle on top of a paper oval. Discuss the similarities and differences.

Do you understand? *What does a circle look like?* [It is completely round. It doesn't have straight sides or corners.]

Reteaching Make a chart, labeling it with a picture of a circle. Ask children to cut out pictures of real-world examples of the shape. Help children glue their examples on the chart.

Directions Have children color the circles.

Topic 14 • Lesson 3

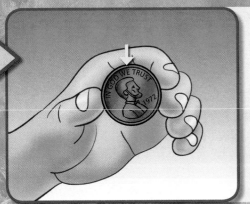

What shape is the coin? [Circle] *How do you know?* [It has no corners. It is round.] *How are a circle and a square different?* [A circle is round, and a square has 4 straight sides.]

What do you see? [A boy holding a disc] *What shape is the disc that the boy is holding?* [It is shaped like a circle.] *How are all the circles the same?* [They are all round.]

Directions Have children mark an X on the objects that are shaped like a circle.

two hundred seventy **270**

Additional Activity

Sorting Flat Shapes

🕐 10 min 👥

Materials Paper squares, rectangles, and circles of different sizes and colors

• Discuss with children the attributes of a circle, a square, and a rectangle.

• Have children place all the circles in one group, all the rectangles in another group, and all the squares in a third group.

• *How is a circle different from a square and a rectangle?* [It doesn't have any corners or sides, and it is round.]

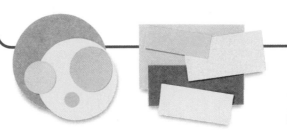

3 **Independent Practice**

Children mark an X on the objects that are shaped like a circle.

Close

Essential Understanding A circle is round and does not have any corners. *A circle is round and does not have any corners. Remember that circles can be different sizes.*

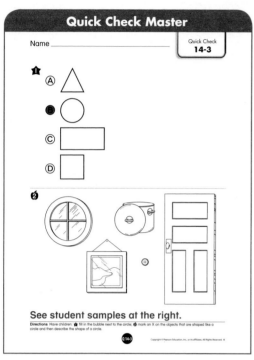

Quick Check Master

Name _____

Quick Check
14-3

See student samples at the right.

Directions Have children: ☆ fill in the bubble next to the circle; ② mark an X on the objects that are shaped like a circle and then describe the shape of a circle.

Q 14-3

Copyright © Pearson Education, Inc., or its affiliates. All Rights Reserved. K

Formative Assessment

Use the **Quick Check** to assess children's understanding.

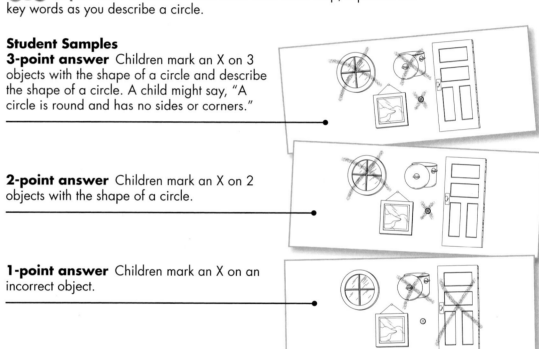

ASSESSMENT

Exercise 1 is worth 1 point.
Use the rubric to score Exercise 2.

Exercise 2
Use Structure Children should be able mark Xs on pictures to identify objects shaped like circles.

ELL Rephrase For children who need additional help, rephrase the key words as you describe a circle.

Student Samples

3-point answer Children mark an X on 3 objects with the shape of a circle and describe the shape of a circle. A child might say, "A circle is round and has no sides or corners."

2-point answer Children mark an X on 2 objects with the shape of a circle.

1-point answer Children mark an X on an incorrect object.

Prescription for Differentiated Instruction
Use children's work on the **Quick Check** to prescribe differentiated instruction.

Points	Prescription
0–2	Intervention
3	On-Level
4	Advanced

Differentiated Instruction

Intervention

Describing Circles

 10 min

Materials (per pair) Circle attribute block

- Provide each pair with a circle attribute block.
- Run your finger around the outside of the circle. *A circle is round and has no corners or sides.* Have children repeat the motion and description.
- Children take turns tracing a circle on their partner's back and describing its shape.

Practice · On-Level · Center Activity

Practice · Advanced · Center Activity

ELL Partner Talk Listen for creative examples as a child describes other objects that can be illustrated by drawing circles.

Leveled Homework

Reteaching Master

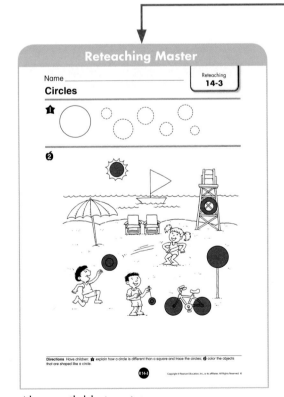

Also available in print

Practice Master

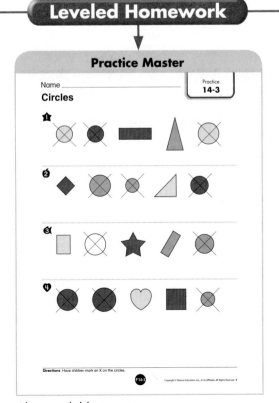

Also available in print

Enrichment Master

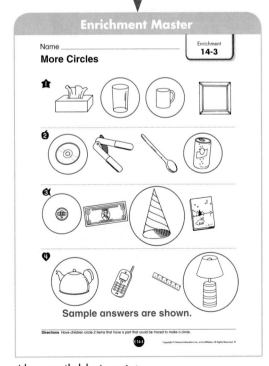

Also available in print

eTools **Geometry Shapes**
www.pearsonsuccessnet.com

eTools **Geometry Shapes**
www.pearsonsuccessnet.com

eTools **Geometry Drawing**
www.pearsonsuccessnet.com

©
Common Core

Domain
Geometry

Cluster
Identify and describe shapes (squares, circles, triangles, rectangles, hexagons, cubes, cones, cylinders, and spheres).

Standard
K.G.2 Correctly name shapes regardless of their orientations or overall size.

Mathematical Practices

☑ Make sense of problems and persevere in solving them.

☑ Reason abstractly and quantitatively.

○ Construct viable arguments and critique the reasoning of others.

○ Model with mathematics.

☑ Use appropriate tools strategically.

☑ Attend to precision.

○ Look for and make use of structure.

○ Look for and express regularity in repeated reasoning.

Triangles

 **Lesson Overview**

Objective	Essential Understanding	Vocabulary	Materials
Children will identify and describe triangles.	All triangles have three sides but can have different configurations of sides and angles.	**triangle**	Triangle attribute blocks (Teaching Tool 36), Triangles (Teaching Tool 22), blunt-tipped scissors, glue

© **PROFESSIONAL DEVELOPMENT**

Math Background

Many young children frequently mix up the names for a triangle and a rectangle when these shapes are shown together. Explain to children that the prefix *tri-* means "three," so the shape with 3 sides is the triangle.

1 Daily Common Core Review

Daily Common Core Review

Name _____

Daily Common
Core Review
14-4

① [rows of cups]
Ⓐ
Ⓑ
Ⓒ
Ⓓ

② [row of apples]
Ⓐ 7
Ⓑ 8
● 9
Ⓓ 10

Directions Have children mark the best answer. ① Which picture shows 2 more cups than the group shown? ② Which number tells how many apples?

Content Reviewed

Exercise 1   Identify 2 More
Exercise 2   Use Numbers to Tell How Many

Also available in print

30 min Problem-Based Interactive Learning

Overview Children will identify shapes that are triangles.

Focus How can you tell if a shape is a triangle?

Materials (per child) Triangle attribute block (Teaching Tool 36), Triangles (Teaching Tool 22), blunt-tipped scissors, glue

Vocabulary triangle

Set the Purpose Remind children that they have learned about rectangles, squares, and circles. *You will learn about a shape called a triangle in this lesson.*

Connect Draw a square and a circle. *Are these shapes the same? Why not?* [No, the circle is round. The square has 4 sides.] *What objects in the classroom have these shapes?* [Answers will vary.]

Use Appropriate Tools
Ask children how attribute blocks would help them learn about shapes.

Academic Vocabulary Distribute a **triangle** attribute block to each child or pairs of children. Hold up a block as you describe it. *This shape is a triangle. It has 3 sides and 3 corners. Tri- means three.* Have children finger-trace around the triangle. *Can you find anything in the classroom that has a shape like a triangle?* [Answers will vary.]

Pose the Problem *Lin is at the lake and wants to find a boat with triangle sails. How can we figure out which sails are shaped like triangles?* Have children share their ideas before you model a possible solution.

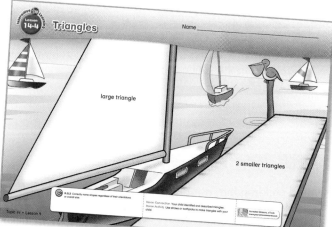

Model Have children cut out the shapes from Teaching Tool 22 or distribute the shapes to them. Hold up the large triangular paper shape and have children do the same. *Is this a triangle?* [Yes] *How many sides does a triangle have?* [3] *How many corners does it have?* [3] Place the large triangle on the left side of the workmat. *Find the large triangle. How do you know it is a triangle?* [It has 3 sides and 3 corners.] Then have them glue it onto the left side of the workmat. Hold up one of the smaller triangles. Discuss why the shape is also a triangle. Have children glue the two smaller triangles onto the right side of the workmat. *These are the shapes of the sails that Lin wanted to find on the sailboats.*

Use Intonation Help children focus on the key vocabulary and key concepts by slightly exaggerating your intonation as you speak.

Small Group Interaction Have partners work together to review square, rectangle, circle, and triangle by drawing each shape. Ask children to identify each shape and tell about its attributes.

How many toothpicks or straws would you need to make a triangle? [3]
How many toothpicks would you need to make a square? [4]

eTools **Geometry Shapes**
www.pearsonsuccessnet.com

Visual Learning

What shape is being traced? [Triangle]
How do you know? [It has 3 sides and 3 corners.]

What do you see? [Lin holding a cracker]
What shape is the cracker? [Triangle]
How are a triangle and a rectangle different? [A triangle has 3 sides and a rectangle has 4 sides.]

1 Visual Learning

Set the Purpose Call children's attention to the **Visual Learning Bridge** at the top of the page. *In this lesson, you will learn about shapes called triangles.*

 Animated Glossary Children can see highlighted words defined in the Online Student Edition.

triangle

www.pearsonsuccessnet.com

2 Guided Practice

Remind children that a triangle has 3 sides, 3 corners, and can be different sizes.

Error Intervention

If children confuse triangles with other shapes,

then have them count the sides of each shape. Have them point to the shapes that have only 3 sides.

Do you understand? *What does a triangle look like?* [It has 3 sides and 3 corners.]

Reteaching Trace paper triangles of different sizes onto cardboard to make templates. Have children choose 2 triangles to trace onto construction paper. Have them cut out their triangles.

Directions Have children color the triangles.

Topic 14 • Lesson 4

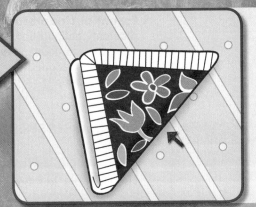

What do you see? [A sailboat with 2 sails] *What shape are the sails?* [Triangles] *How do you know?* [Each sail has 3 sides.] *How are a triangle and a circle different?* [A triangle has 3 straight sides, and a circle is round.]

What do you see? [A napkin] *What shape is the napkin?* [Triangle] *How are all the triangles the same?* [They all have 3 straight sides and 3 corners.]

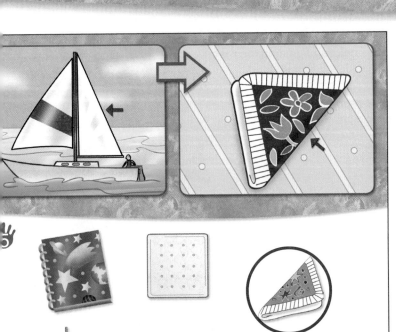

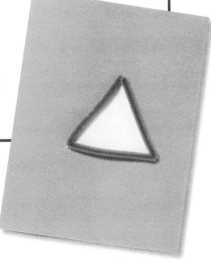

Additional Activity

Triangle Books

🕐 15 min 👥

Materials Precut construction paper triangles of different sizes, shapes, and colors; (per pair) sheet of construction paper, glue, blunt-tipped scissors, yarn, pipe cleaners

- Have children work in pairs. Give each pair a triangle.
- Have children glue the triangle onto their sheet of construction paper. Then have them glue yarn or pipe cleaners around the outline of the triangle.
- Put the children's pictures together to create a class book about triangles.

Directions Have children circle the objects that are shaped like a triangle.

two hundred seventy-two **272**

3 **Independent Practice**

Children circle the objects that are shaped like a triangle.

272A

Close

Essential Understanding All triangles have three sides but can have different configurations of sides and angles. *Triangles have three sides and three corners. Remember that triangles have sides that can be the same length or different lengths.*

 **ASSESSMENT**

Exercise 1 is worth 1 point.
Use the rubric to score Exercise 2.

Exercise 2

Reason Abstractly Children should be able to color pictures to identify objects shaped like triangles.

ELL Use Repetition For children who need additional help, have them repeat descriptions of shapes before beginning their work.

Student Samples
3-point answer Children color 3 objects with the shape of a triangle and describe the shape of a triangle. A child might say, "A triangle has 3 sides and 3 corners."

2-point answer Children color 2 objects with the shape of a triangle.

1-point answer Children color an incorrect object.

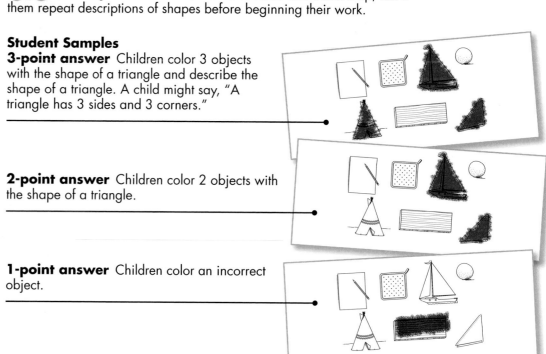

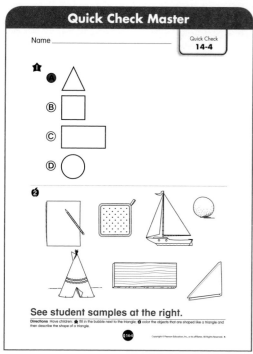

 Formative Assessment

Use the **Quick Check** to assess children's understanding.

Prescription for Differentiated Instruction
Use children's work on the **Quick Check** to prescribe differentiated instruction.

Points	Prescription
0–2	Intervention
3	On-Level
4	Advanced

Differentiated Instruction

Intervention

Back to the Drawing Board

 10 min

Materials Construction paper, markers, (per pair) crayons

- On a sheet of paper, draw an outline of a circle with a marker using small dots or dashes. Draw outlines of different types of triangles on separate sheets of paper.

- Partner A chooses a drawing, traces the shape with a crayon, and asks Partner B to identify it.

- Partners switch roles and repeat the activity.

On-Level

Practice · On-Level · Center Activity

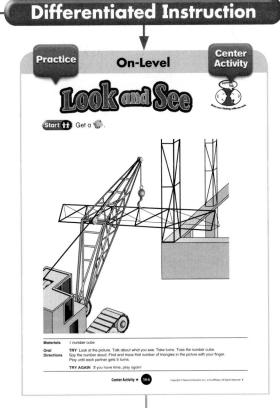

Advanced

Practice · Advanced · Center Activity

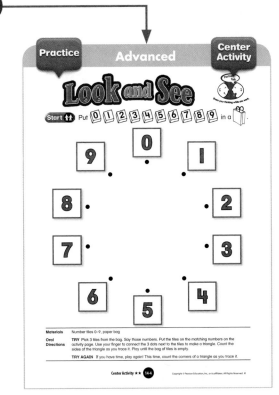

ELL Report Back To check understanding, ask a child to repeat and complete this sentence: *A triangle has 3 corners and _____.* [3 sides]

Leveled Homework

Reteaching Master

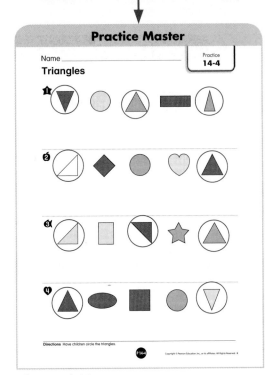

Also available in print

Practice Master

Also available in print

Enrichment Master

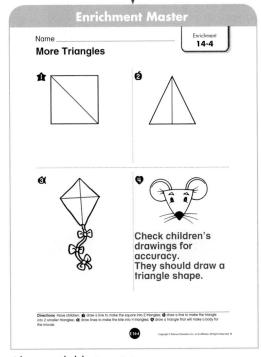

Also available in print

Domain

Geometry

Cluster

Identify and describe shapes (squares, circles, triangles, rectangles, hexagons, cubes, cones, cylinders, and spheres).

Standard

K.G.2 Correctly name shapes regardless of their orientations or overall size.

Mathematical Practices

☑ Make sense of problems and persevere in solving them.

☑ Reason abstractly and quantitatively.

○ Construct viable arguments and critique the reasoning of others.

○ Model with mathematics.

☑ Use appropriate tools strategically.

☑ Attend to precision.

○ Look for and make use of structure.

○ Look for and express regularity in repeated reasoning.

Hexagons

 **Lesson Overview**

Objective	Essential Understanding	Vocabulary	Materials
Children will identify and describe hexagons.	A hexagon is a shape with six sides and six corners.	**hexagon**	Hexagon pattern blocks (Teaching Tool 35), Hexagons (Teaching Tool 23), blunt-tipped scissors, glue

© PROFESSIONAL DEVELOPMENT

Math Background

Research says . . . geometric thinking develops slowly over time as children take part in first informal experiences, then in more formal experiences with shapes and relationships (van Hiele, 1986).

1 Daily Common Core Review

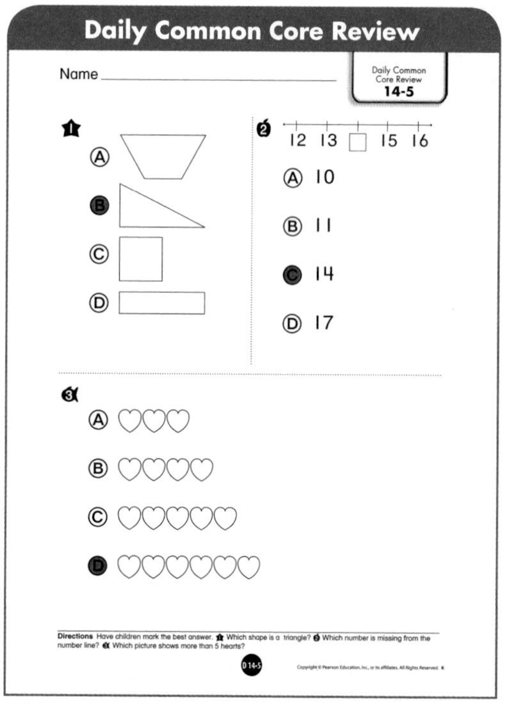

Daily Common Core Review

Name _____

Daily Common Core Review
14-5

⭐ Ⓐ Ⓑ Ⓒ Ⓓ

❷ 12 13 ☐ 15 16
Ⓐ 10
Ⓑ 11
● 14
Ⓓ 17

❸ Ⓐ ♡♡♡
Ⓑ ♡♡♡♡
Ⓒ ♡♡♡♡♡
● ♡♡♡♡♡♡

Directions Have children mark the best answer. ⭐ Which shape is a triangle? ❷ Which number is missing from the number line? ❸ Which picture shows more than 5 hearts?

○14-5

Copyright © Pearson Education, Inc., or its affiliates. All Rights Reserved.

Also available in print

Content Reviewed

Exercise 1   Identify Two-Dimensional Shapes

Exercise 2   Order Numbers to 20

Exercise 3   Compare Quantities

 30 min # Problem-Based Interactive Learning

Overview Children will identify shapes that are hexagons.

Focus How can you tell if a shape is a hexagon?

Materials (per child) Hexagon pattern block (Teaching Tool 35), Hexagons (Teaching Tool 23), blunt-tipped scissors, glue

Vocabulary hexagon

Set the Purpose Remind children that they have learned about rectangles, squares, circles, and triangles. *You will learn about another shape in this lesson.*

Connect Review with children the 4 shapes that they have learned. Draw 4 simple shape outlines on the board and ask questions such as: *How many sides does a triangle have?* [3] *How many corners does it have?* [3] Ask similar questions about the attributes of a rectangle, a square, and a circle.

MATHEMATICAL
PRACTICES

Use Appropriate Tools
Ask children what tools they could use to help them determine what is and is not a hexagon.

Academic Vocabulary Distribute a yellow **hexagon** pattern block to each child or pairs of children. Hold up a block as you describe it. *This shape is a hexagon. A hexagon has 6 sides and 6 corners.* As you describe the hexagon, point to and count the sides together with children. Then count the corners together.

Pose the Problem *The HEXAGONS Art Gallery needs new pieces of art. Only art with hexagons can be put in the gallery. How can you make new pieces of art for the gallery?* Have children share their ideas before modeling a solution.

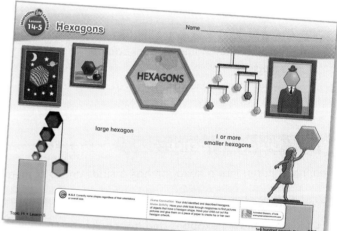

Model Have children cut out the paper hexagons from Teaching Tool 23 or distribute the shapes to them. Hold up the large hexagonal paper shape. *Could this shape be a frame for a picture in the art gallery?* [Yes] *How do you know?* [It is a hexagon. It has 6 sides and 6 corners.] *Let's draw a picture in the frame.* Model drawing a simple picture inside the frame, such as a plant with a flower shaped like a hexagon. Have children do the same. *Now let's put our picture in the art gallery.* Have children glue the paper hexagon onto the left side of the workmat.

Small-Group Interaction Have partners work together to complete the student page as you pose another problem. *The HEXAGONS Art Gallery needs 1 more piece of art. How can you use hexagons to make a new piece of art?* Have children use 1 or more of the smaller paper hexagons to make a picture, such as a snowman statue, and glue it onto the right side of their workmat. Have volunteers share their pictures.

 Show a stop sign. *Is a stop sign a hexagon?* [No] *Why not?* [It has 8 sides and 8 corners. A hexagon has 6 sides and 6 corners.]

eTools **Geometry Shapes**
www.pearsonsuccessnet.com

Visual Learning

What shape do you see? [Hexagon] *How do you know?* [It has 6 sides and 6 corners.] *How are a hexagon and a rectangle different?* [A rectangle has 4 sides and 4 corners.]

What do you see? [Honeycomb] *What shape is the honeycomb?* [Hexagon] *How are a circle and a hexagon different?* [A circle has no sides. It is round.]

1 Visual Learning

Set the Purpose Call children's attention to the **Visual Learning Bridge** at the top of the page. *In this lesson, you will learn about shapes called hexagons.*

 Animated Glossary Children can see highlighted words defined in the Online Student Edition.

hexagon

www.pearsonsuccessnet.com

2 Guided Practice

Remind children that a hexagon has 6 sides and 6 corners.

Error Intervention

If children confuse hexagons and trapezoids,

then have them use pattern blocks to show how trapezoids can be used to make a hexagon.

Do you understand? *What does a hexagon look like?* [It has 6 sides and 6 corners.]

Reteaching Have children trace the outline of a hexagon with their fingers. *A hexagon has 6 sides and 6 corners.* Have children repeat the motion and the description. Children take turns tracing a hexagon on their partner's back and describing the shape.

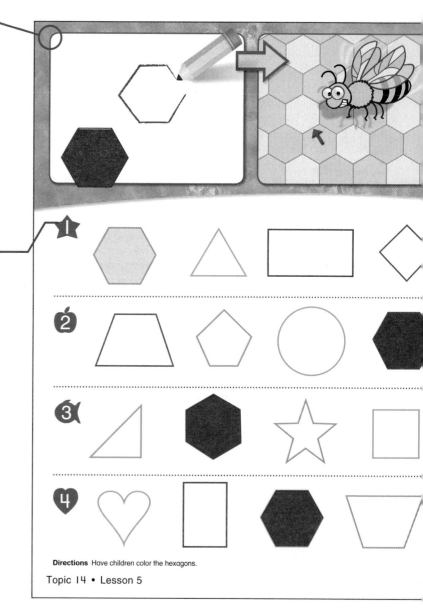

Directions Have children color the hexagons.

Topic 14 • Lesson 5

What do you see? [A window] *What shape is the window?* [Hexagon] *How are a triangle and a hexagon different?* [A triangle has 3 sides and 3 corners.]

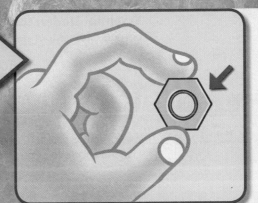

What do you see? [A nut] *What shape is the nut?* [Hexagon] *How are a square and a hexagon different?* [A square has 4 sides, and 4 corners, with 4 equal sides.]

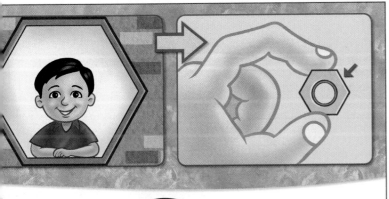

Additional Activity

Hexagon Art

🕐 15 min 👥

Materials Paper hexagons in assorted sizes and colors, sheet of white paper, glue, crayons or markers

- Have children use the hexagonal paper shapes and crayons or markers to make pictures.
- Partners work together to arrange their hexagons into a picture and glue them to their paper.
- Have partners share their pictures. Then display children's pictures in a classroom art gallery.

ections Have children circle the objects that are shaped like a hexagon.

3 **Independent Practice**

Have children circle the objects that are shaped like a hexagon.

274A

Close

Essential Understanding A hexagon is a shape with six sides and six corners. *Remember that hexagons have six sides and six corners.*

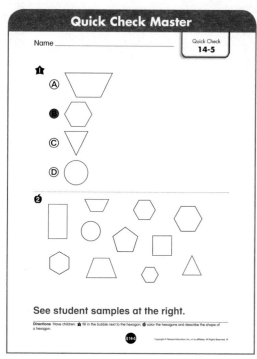

Formative Assessment

Use the **Quick Check** to assess children's understanding.

 **ASSESSMENT**

Exercise 1 is worth 1 point.
Use the rubric to score Exercise 2.

Exercise 2
Reason Abstractly Children should be able to color pictures to identify the hexagons.

ELL Use Repetition For children who need additional help following directions, have them repeat key words and phrases before beginning their work.

Student Samples
3-point answer Children correctly color 4 hexagons and describe the shape of a hexagon. A child might say, "A hexagon has 6 sides and 6 corners."

2-point answer Children color 2 or 3 hexagons.

1-point answer Children color an incorrect shape.

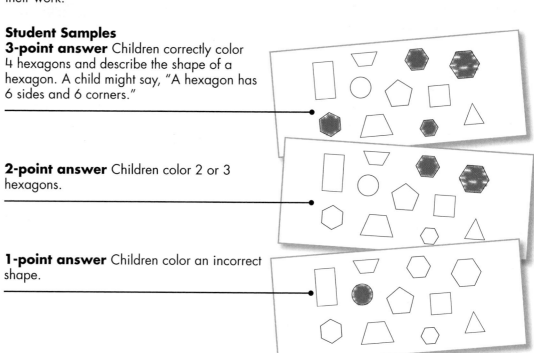

Prescription for Differentiated Instruction
Use children's work on the **Quick Check** to prescribe differentiated instruction.

Points	Prescription
0–2	Intervention
3	On-Level
4	Advanced

Differentiated Instruction

Intervention

What's in the Bag?

 15 min

Materials Paper bag, attribute blocks (or Teaching Tool 36), pattern blocks (or Teaching Tool 35): hexagon, square, triangle

- Place an assortment of blocks in the bag. Reach in and choose one of the blocks. Hold it up and model naming and describing it. For example, *This is a hexagon. It has 6 sides. It has 6 corners.*

- Have children take turns choosing a block, and then naming and describing it. Encourage children to describe the shape using 2 attributes, for example, "My shape is a triangle. It has 3 sides. It has 3 corners."

On-Level

Practice | **Center Activity**

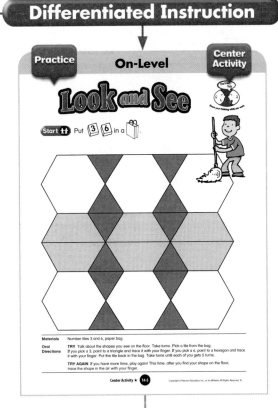

Look and See

Start ↑↑ Put 3 6 in a

Materials Number tiles 3 and 6, paper bag

Oral Directions **TRY** Talk about the shapes you see on the floor. Take turns. Pick a tile from the bag. If you pick a 3, point to a triangle and trace it with your finger. If you pick a 6, point to a hexagon and trace it with your finger. Put the tile back in the bag. Take turns until each of you gets 5 turns.

TRY AGAIN If you have more time, play again! This time, after you find your shape on the floor, trace the shape in the air with your finger.

Center Activity ★ 14-5   Copyright © Pearson Education, Inc., or its affiliates. All Rights Reserved. 8

Advanced

Practice | **Center Activity**

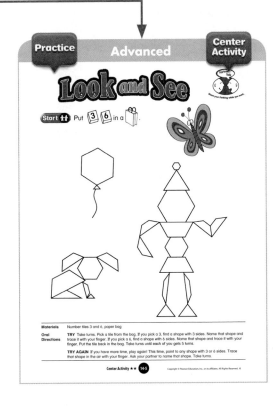

Look and See

Start ↑↑ Put 3 6 in a

Materials Number tiles 3 and 6, paper bag

Oral Directions **TRY** Take turns. Pick a tile from the bag. If you pick a 3, find a shape with 3 sides. Name that shape and trace it with your finger. If you pick a 6, find a shape with 6 sides. Name that shape and trace it with your finger. Put the tile back in the bag. Take turns until each of you gets 5 turns.

TRY AGAIN If you have more time, play again! This time, point to any shape with 3 or 6 sides. Trace that shape in the air with your finger. Ask your partner to name that shape. Take turns.

Center Activity ★★ 14-5   Copyright © Pearson Education, Inc., or its affiliates. All Rights Reserved. 8

ELL **Report Back** To check understanding, ask a child to repeat and complete this sentence: *A shape that has 6 sides and 6 corners is a ___.* [Hexagon]

Leveled Homework

Reteaching Master

Name _____
Hexagons

Reteaching 14-5

1.
2.
3.
4.
5.
6.

Directions Have children circle the hexagon.

R14-5   Copyright © Pearson Education, Inc., or its affiliates. All Rights Reserved. 8

Also available in print

 eTools **Geometry Shapes**
www.pearsonsuccessnet.com

Practice Master

Name _____
Hexagons

Practice 14-5

1.
2.
3.
4.

Directions Have children circle the hexagons.

P14-5   Copyright © Pearson Education, Inc., or its affiliates. All Rights Reserved. 8

Also available in print

 eTools **Geometry Shapes**
www.pearsonsuccessnet.com

Enrichment Master

Name _____
Draw With Dots

Enrichment 14-5

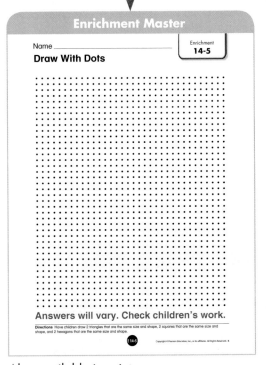

Answers will vary. Check children's work.

Directions Have children draw 2 triangles that are the same size and shape, 2 squares that are the same size and shape, and 2 hexagons that are the same size and shape.

E14-5   Copyright © Pearson Education, Inc., or its affiliates. All Rights Reserved. 8

Also available in print

 eTools **Geometry Drawing**
www.pearsonsuccessnet.com

Lesson
14-6

Common Core

Domain
Geometry

Cluster
Identify and describe shapes (squares, circles, triangles, rectangles, hexagons, cubes, cones, cylinders, and spheres).

Standard
K.G.3 Identify shapes as two-dimensional (lying in a plane, "flat") or three-dimensional ("solid"). Also **K.G.2**

Mathematical Practices
- ✔ Make sense of problems and persevere in solving them.
- ✔ Reason abstractly and quantitatively.
- ○ Construct viable arguments and critique the reasoning of others.
- ○ Model with mathematics.
- ✔ Use appropriate tools strategically.
- ✔ Attend to precision.
- ✔ Look for and make use of structure.
- ○ Look for and express regularity in repeated reasoning.

Solid Figures

Quick and Easy Lesson Overview

Objective	Essential Understanding	Vocabulary	Materials
Children will identify cubes, cones, cylinders, and spheres and relate them to real-life objects.	Three-dimensional or solid figures have length, width, and height. Many everyday objects closely approximate standard geometric solids.	**cone** **cylinder** **sphere** **cube**	Classroom objects in the shape of solid figures, Solid Figures (Teaching Tool 24), blunt-tipped scissors, glue, geometric solids: cone, cylinder, sphere, cube

PROFESSIONAL DEVELOPMENT

Math Background

Children benefit greatly by seeing connections between geometric shapes and real-world objects. Provide geometric models and manipulatives to help children identify different shapes and their parts.

1 Daily Common Core Review

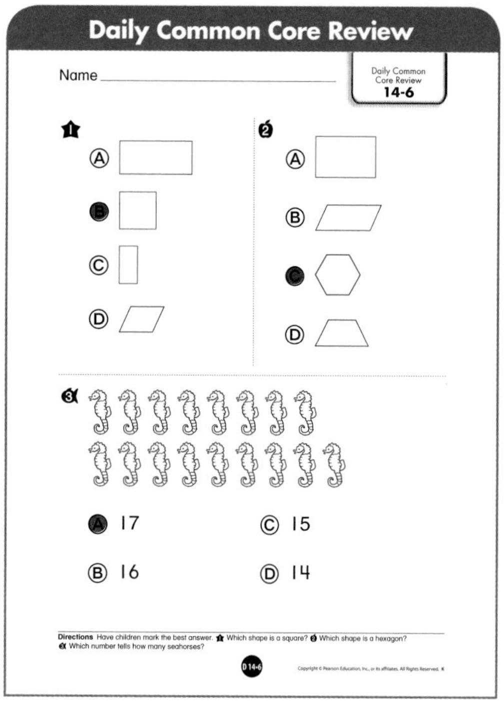
Daily Common Core Review

Name

Daily Common Core Review 14-6

1. Ⓐ Ⓑ Ⓒ Ⓓ

2. Ⓐ Ⓑ Ⓒ Ⓓ

3. Ⓐ 17 Ⓒ 15 Ⓑ 16 Ⓓ 14

Directions Have children mark the best answer. 1. Which shape is a square? 2. Which shape is a hexagon? 3. Which number tells how many seahorses?

D 14-6

Also available in print

Content Reviewed
Exercises 1–2 Identify Two-Dimensional Shapes
Exercise 3 Use Numbers to Tell How Many

 30 min **Problem-Based Interactive Learning**

Overview Children will describe and identify three-dimensional shapes and identify everyday objects that have the same shapes.

Focus What do you look for when you describe and match shapes?

Materials Classroom objects in the shape of solid figures, Solid Figures (Teaching Tool 24), blunt-tipped scissors, glue, geometric solids: cone, cylinder, sphere, cube

Vocabulary **cone**, **cylinder**, **sphere**, **cube**

 **Set the Purpose** Remind children that they have learned about flat shapes. *You will learn more about the shapes of many classroom objects in this lesson.*

Connect Draw a circle, square, rectangle, triangle, and hexagon on the board. Point to each shape as children say aloud the names.

 MATHEMATICAL PRACTICES

Reason Abstractly Ask children how they would find matching shapes.

Academic Vocabulary Display a set of solids: **cone**, **cylinder**, **sphere**, **cube**. These shapes are called solid figures. Hold up each solid, name it, and point out its special features. *The cone has a flat side and a curved side. The cube has many flat sides.* [Point to some of them.] *I can also count its corners. Does the cylinder have corners?* [No] *Does it have flat sides?* [Yes] *How many?* [2]

Pose the Problem *Lin wants to find objects that have the same shape as solid figures. How can she find out which objects have the same shape?* Have children share their ideas.

Model Hold up the sphere and name it. *This is called a sphere.* Have children repeat the name. *Does this shape have flat sides?* [No] *Does it have any corners?* [No] *No, it is round like a ball.* Place a ball near the sphere. *This object has the same shape.* Invite children to find other objects that have the same shape and place them near the sphere. *Find a picture that looks like this solid figure.* Have children cut out pictures of the solid figures. Then have them glue the picture in the first box on their workmat. Continue in this manner with the cube. *Does a cube have corners?* [Yes] *Does it have sides?* [Yes] *How many sides?* [6] *What objects in our classroom have this shape?* [Sample answers: blocks, tissue box] *Let's find a picture that looks like this solid figure.* Introduce the cylinder and the cone by having children repeat each name, identify the shapes' attributes, and find a matching picture. Point out that a cone has 1 flat side and that a cylinder has 2 flat sides. Then have children glue the pictures in the boxes on the student page.

Extend Show children various classroom objects shaped like solid figures. Have them complete this sentence for each object: *This object is shaped like a _____.* [Sphere, cube, cone, or cylinder]

What is Lin holding? [Present] *What shape does it have?* [Cube] *What things in our classroom have that shape?* [Accept all reasonable answers such as box, crate, and block.]

What is Lin holding? [Can of soup] *What shape does it have?* [Cylinder] *Can you name other things that have that shape?* [Accept all reasonable answers such as juice cans and water bottles.]

1 Visual Learning

Set the Purpose Call children's attention to the **Visual Learning Bridge** at the top of the page. *In this lesson, you will learn about these solid figures: cube, cylinder, cone, and sphere.*

 Animated Glossary Children can see highlighted words defined in the Online Student Edition.

cone, cylinder, sphere, cube

www.pearsonsuccessnet.com

2 Guided Practice

Remind children that matching shapes do not need to be the same size or color.

Error Intervention

If children are confused by the size, color, or orientation of a solid figure,

then have them compare models with matching classroom objects. Focus on the attributes of one shape at a time.

Do you understand? *Name something in our classroom that has the shape of a cube.* [Accept all reasonable answers.] Repeat for cone, cylinder, and sphere.

Reteaching Have pairs of children handle the set of geometric solids. Name the shapes, one at a time, and have children repeat the names and describe the shapes using the words *corner* and *side*. Then hold up each solid figure and have children find or name an object in the classroom that has the same shape.

Directions Have children name the solid figure on the left and then circle the matching figure on the right.

Topic 14 • Lesson 6

What solid figure looks like a party hat? [Cone] *Name something with that shape.* [Accept all reasonable answers, such as ice cream cone and toy top.]

What shape does a ball have? [It is round and has no flat sides.] *What solid figure looks like a ball?* [A sphere] *Can you name other things that have that shape?* [Accept all reasonable answers, such as the planet Earth, the sun, and peas.]

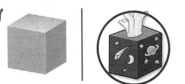

ctions Have children name the solid figure on the left and then circle the object on the right that has the same shape.

Additional Activity

Sorting Solid Figures

🕐 10 min 🏃

Materials Classroom objects in the shape of solid figures, 4 large sheets of construction paper (18" x 24"), geometric solids: cube, cylinder, sphere, cone

- Place a different solid figure on each sheet of paper.
- Assign each child a solid figure. Have him or her find one classroom object that has the same shape as the assigned solid and place that object on the appropriate sheet of paper.
- Reassign solids and repeat the activity.
- Then hold up each classroom object and have children tell how it is the same as the solid figure.

3 Independent Practice

Children name each solid figure. They circle the object with the same shape.

Close

Essential Understanding Three-dimensional or solid figures have length, width, and height. Many everyday objects closely approximate standard geometric solids. *There are special names for solid figures. Remember to look for flat sides and corners when you describe and match solid shapes.*

ASSESSMENT

Exercise 1 is worth 1 point.
Use the rubric to score Exercise 2.

Exercise 2

Reason Abstractly Children should be able to color 3 objects with the same shape and identify them as spheres.

ELL Model Thinking Aloud Help children describe the objects by characteristics such as flat sides and corners. *The baseball is round. The can has a curved side and 2 flat sides. The ball does not have the same shape as the cylinder.*

Student Samples
3-point answer Children color 3 matching objects and identify the figures as spheres.

2-point answer Children color 2 matching objects and identify the figures as spheres.

1-point answer Children color 1 item.

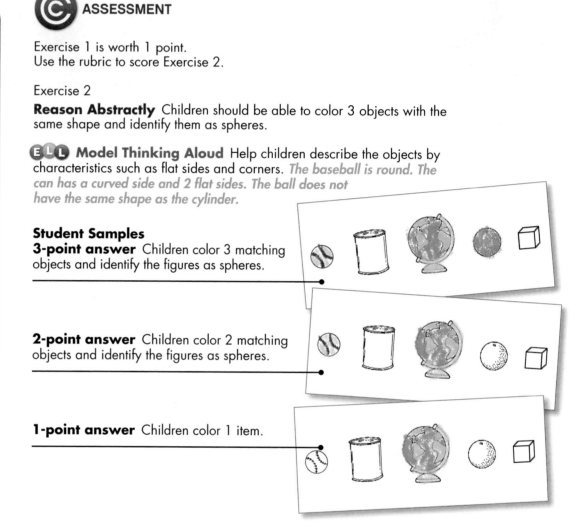

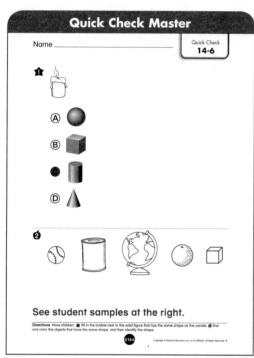

Formative Assessment

Use the **Quick Check** to assess children's understanding.

Prescription for Differentiated Instruction
Use children's work on the **Quick Check** to prescribe differentiated instruction.

Points	Prescription
0–2	Intervention
3	On-Level
4	Advanced

Differentiated Instruction

Intervention

Match and Name

  10 min

Materials (per pair) Classroom objects in the shape of solid figures, geometric solids: cube, cylinder, sphere, cone

- Show children a sphere. *This is a sphere.* Have children repeat "sphere."

- Model describing a sphere. *A sphere is round like a ball. It has no corners.*

- Ask pairs of children to find an object with the same shape as the sphere. Have each pair show the object, name it, and describe the shape.

- Repeat the activity with the 3 other solid figures: cube, cone, and cylinder.

On-Level

Practice | Center Activity

Play a Game

Start ↟↟ Get a ⬤.

Get 1 blue square.
Get 1 red square.

Materials 1 number cube, 1 blue square, 1 red square
Oral Directions **TRY** Put both squares on the ship. Take turns. Toss the number cube. Say the number aloud. Count that number of solid figures. Name the solid figure on which you land. If the solid figure is a sphere or a cylinder, move your square forward 1 space. If your shape does not look like a sphere or a cylinder, keep your square where it is. The first player to get to the treasure chest wins.

TRY AGAIN If you have time, play again!

Center Activity ★ 14-6   Copyright © Pearson Education, Inc., or its affiliates. All Rights Reserved. K

Advanced

Practice | Center Activity

Play a Game

Start ↟↟ Get a ⬤.

Get 1 blue square.
Get 1 red square.

Materials 1 number cube, 1 blue square, 1 red square
Oral Directions **TRY** Put both squares on the ship. Take turns. Toss the number cube. Say the number aloud. Count that number of solid figures. Name the solid figure on which you land. Name any object you have seen outside, in your classroom, or at home that looks like that solid figure. Then cover the figure with your colored square. The first player to get to the treasure chest wins.

TRY AGAIN If you have time, play again!

Center Activity ★★ 14-6   Copyright © Pearson Education, Inc., or its affiliates. All Rights Reserved. K

E L L Partner Talk Listen for the name of a solid figure followed by an object with the same shape. For example, a child might say, "This is a cube. It looks like a building block."

Leveled Homework

Reteaching Master

Name _____
Solid Figures

Reteaching
14-6

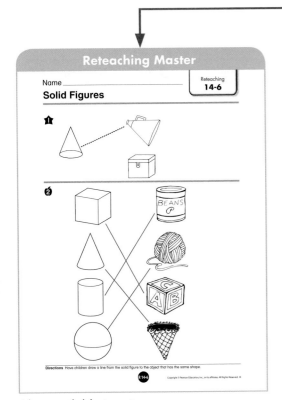

Directions Have children draw a line from the solid figure to the object that has the same shape.

R 14-6   Copyright © Pearson Education, Inc., or its affiliates. All Rights Reserved. K

Also available in print

Practice Master

Name _____
Solid Figures

Practice
14-6

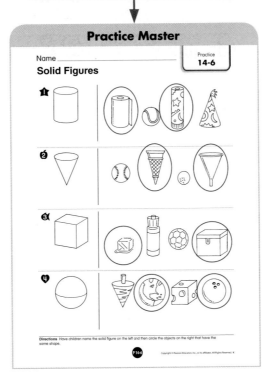

Directions Have children name the solid figure on the left and then circle the objects on the right that have the same shape.

P 14-6   Copyright © Pearson Education, Inc., or its affiliates. All Rights Reserved. K

Also available in print

Enrichment Master

Name _____
Shape Match-Up

Enrichment
14-6

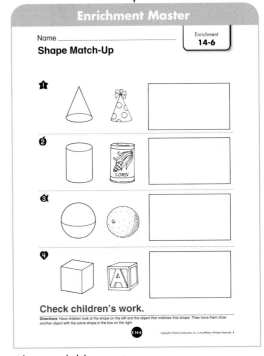

Check children's work.

Directions Have children look at the shape on the left and the object that matches that shape. Then have them draw another object with the same shape in the box on the right.

E 14-6   Copyright © Pearson Education, Inc., or its affiliates. All Rights Reserved. K

Also available in print

Domain

Geometry

Cluster

Identify and describe shapes (squares, circles, triangles, rectangles, hexagons, cubes, cones, cylinders, and spheres).

Standard

K.G.3 Identify shapes as two-dimensional (lying in a plane, "flat") or three-dimensional ("solid"). Also **K.G.2**

Mathematical Practices

○ Make sense of problems and persevere in solving them.

☑ Reason abstractly and quantitatively.

○ Construct viable arguments and critique the reasoning of others.

○ Model with mathematics.

☑ Use appropriate tools strategically.

☑ Attend to precision.

☑ Look for and make use of structure.

○ Look for and express regularity in repeated reasoning.

Flat Surfaces of Solid Figures

 **Lesson Overview**

Objective	Essential Understanding	Vocabulary	Materials
Children will identify three-dimensional figures and describe the shape of flat surfaces.	The flat surfaces of many solid figures have specific shapes.	**flat surface**	Classroom objects in the shape of solid figures, geometric solids: cone, cylinder, cube, rectangular prism, pyramid

© **PROFESSIONAL DEVELOPMENT**

Math Background

Some three-dimensional solids have faces, like boxes. The faces of these solid figures are two-dimensional shapes, like squares. Be careful to distinguish the attributes and names of solid figures versus flat shapes and do not use the same name for different attributes. For example, do not call a sphere a circle. It is round but it is not a circle.

1 Daily Common Core Review

Daily Common Core Review

Name _____

Daily Common Core Review **14-7**

❶ ☆☆☆☆☆☆
☆☆☆

ⓐ 10

Ⓑ 8

ⓒ 7

ⓓ 4

❷ ⓐ △

Ⓑ □

ⓒ ▭

ⓓ ○

❸ 🐕🐕🐕🐕🐕🐕

ⓐ 2 ⓒ 5

Ⓑ 4 Ⓓ 6

Directions Have children mark the best answer. ❶ Which number tells how many stars? ❷ Which shape is a triangle? ❸ Which number tells how many puppies?

© 14-7 Copyright © Pearson Education, Inc., or its affiliates. All Rights Reserved.

Also available in print

Content Reviewed

Exercise 1   Use Numbers to Tell How Many

Exercise 2   Identify Two-Dimensional Shapes

Exercise 3   Use Numbers to Tell How Many

 30 min # Problem-Based Interactive Learning

 Hands-On Minds-On

Overview Children will examine, trace, and describe flat surfaces of solid figures.

Focus How can you describe the flat surfaces of solids?

Materials Classroom objects in the shape of solid figures, geometric solids: cone, cylinder, cube, rectangular prism, pyramid

Vocabulary flat surface

 **Engage**

Set the Purpose Remind children that they have learned about different solid figures. *You will learn about the shapes of the flat sides of solid figures in this lesson.*

Connect Ask children to name real-life objects that are three-dimensional and have flat sides. If possible, provide some of these objects for children to check their answers.

MATHEMATICAL PRACTICES

Reason Abstractly
Ask children how they could apply what they learned about shapes and solids to help them identify the flat surfaces of solid objects.

Academic Vocabulary *Many objects have flat sides that are called* flat surfaces. Hold up some objects, pointing out the flat surfaces (the sides of blocks, the bottom of a calculator, the cover of a book).

Pose the Problem Draw or trace a circle on the board. *Lin needs to draw this shape for a project. This is a circle. Which solid figure has a flat surface that is this shape when traced?* Have children try to draw the circle and then share their ideas for a possible solution.

Model Display the cone and touch the curved surface. *This surface is curved.* Touch the flat surface. *The cone has 1 flat surface.* Trace the flat surface on the board. *Does this match the shape on the board?* [Yes] *What other solid has a flat surface like this?* [Cylinder] *How are the cylinder and the cone alike?* [Their flat surfaces look the same. They each have a round part.] *How many flat surfaces does a cylinder have?* [2] Trace a flat surface of the cylinder on the board. *What shape are the flat surfaces?* [Circles] Then have children use a solid figure or a classroom object to trace a flat surface on their left workmat. [Cone, cylinder] *Look at the cube. Does it have flat surfaces?* [Yes] *Are they all the same shape?* [Yes] *Are they all the same size?* [Yes] Trace a flat surface of the cube on the board. *What shape are the flat surfaces?* [Squares]

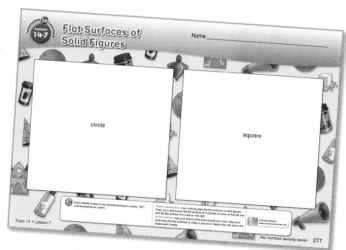

Small-Group Interaction Draw a square on the board. *What solid figure could we trace to make this shape?* [Cube] Have partners work together to find a classroom object with the same shape and trace a flat surface on their right workmat.

 Extend

Display the rectangular prism and the pyramid. Point out the flat surfaces of each solid figure without naming it. Call on volunteers to trace a flat side of each solid on the board and name the shape they draw.

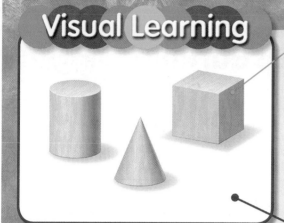

Visual Learning

What solid figures do you see? [Cube, cone, cylinder]

What part of the solid figure is being traced? [A flat surface] *What does the traced shape look like?* [It is square. It has straight edges.] *Can you name an object that has square flat surfaces?* [Box, block]

1 Visual Learning

Set the Purpose Call children's attention to the **Visual Learning Bridge** at the top of the page. *In this lesson, you will learn about the flat surfaces of solid figures.*

 Animated Glossary Children can see highlighted words defined in the Online Student Edition.

flat surface

www.pearsonsuccessnet.com

2 Guided Practice

Remind children that shapes can be in different positions.

Error Intervention

If children have difficulty with the orientation of shapes,

then provide real objects as they complete the exercises.

Do you understand? *What do the flat surfaces of a cube look like?* [They are square, and they are all the same size.] *What do the flat surfaces of a cylinder look like?* [They are round, and they are the same size.]

Reteaching Give each child a solid figure (cube, cone, cylinder) or a classroom object with one of these shapes. Model how to use a solid figure or object to trace each flat surface on paper. Then have each child trace the flat surface, or surfaces, of his or her object. Have children share their tracings and talk about the objects that have those flat surfaces.

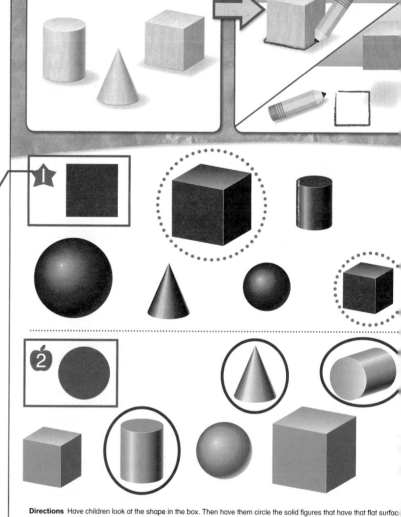

Directions Have children look at the shape in the box. Then have them circle the solid figures that have that flat surface.

Topic 14 • Lesson 7

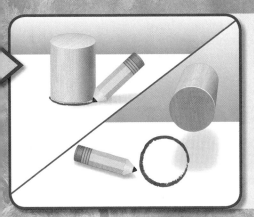

What part of the solid figure is being traced? [A flat surface] *What does the traced shape look like?* [It is a circle. It is round.] *Can you name an object that has the same flat surface?* [Jar]

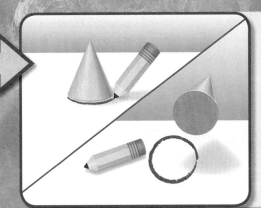

What part of the solid figure is being traced? [The flat surface] *What does the traced shape look like?* [It is a circle. It is round.]

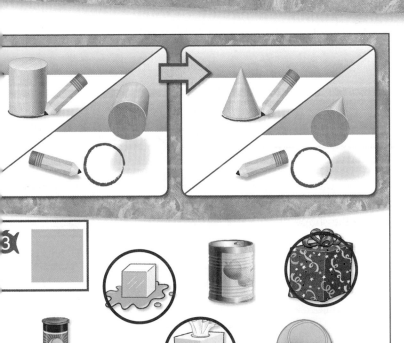

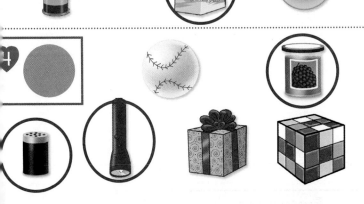

rections Have children look at the shape in the box. Then have them circle the objects that have that flat surface.

two hundred seventy-eight 278

Additional Activity

Counting Flat Surfaces

⏱ 10 min

Materials (per group) Self-stick notes, geometric solids: cube, cylinder, sphere, cone

- Hold up a cone. *How can you find out the number of flat surfaces on a cone?* [Count them.]

- Have group members find and count the flat surface on the cone, write the number on a self-stick note, and label the object. Repeat with each solid.

- Have children order the shapes from fewest to most flat surfaces and compare.

---

3 **Independent Practice**

Children circle the objects with flat surfaces that match the shape in the box.

278A

Close

Essential Understanding The flat surfaces of many solid figures have specific shapes. *The flat surfaces of solid figures have special shapes. Remember that you can trace the flat surface of a solid figure to see what shape it is.*

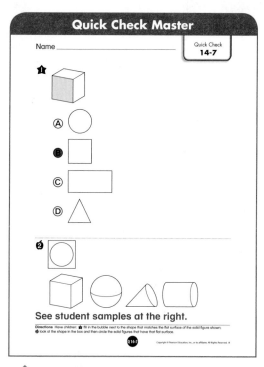

Formative Assessment

Use the **Quick Check** to assess children's understanding.

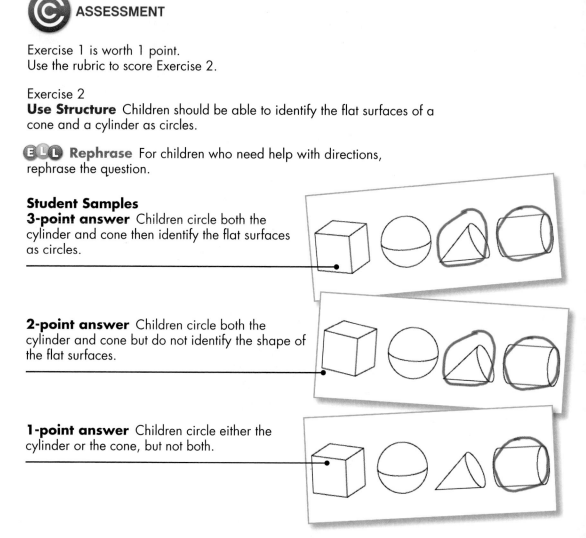

ASSESSMENT

Exercise 1 is worth 1 point.
Use the rubric to score Exercise 2.

Exercise 2
Use Structure Children should be able to identify the flat surfaces of a cone and a cylinder as circles.

ELL Rephrase For children who need help with directions, rephrase the question.

Student Samples
3-point answer Children circle both the cylinder and cone then identify the flat surfaces as circles.

2-point answer Children circle both the cylinder and cone but do not identify the shape of the flat surfaces.

1-point answer Children circle either the cylinder or the cone, but not both.

Prescription for Differentiated Instruction
Use children's work on the **Quick Check** to prescribe differentiated instruction.

Points	Prescription
0–2	Intervention
3	On-Level
4	Advanced

Differentiated Instruction

Intervention

Flat Surfaces and Not-Flat Surfaces

 10 min

Materials (per pair) Modeling clay, rolling pin, geometric solids: cube, cylinder, sphere, cone

- Hold up the cube and rub your palm across the sides. *These are flat surfaces.* Hold up the sphere, cupping your hand around it. *There are no flat surfaces on a sphere.* Ask children to pick up each shape and verbally identify the flat and curved surfaces.

- Have partners make imprints of the flat surfaces in rolled-out clay.

On-Level

Practice · **Center Activity**

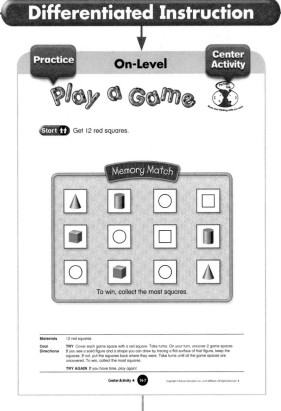

Advanced

Practice · **Center Activity**

ELL Report Back To check understanding, ask a child to repeat and complete this sentence: *2 solid figures we can use to trace a circle are _____.* [A cone and a cylinder]

Leveled Homework

Reteaching Master

Also available in print

Practice Master

Also available in print

Enrichment Master

Also available in print

14-8

Domain
Geometry

Cluster
Identify and describe shapes (squares, circles, triangles, rectangles, hexagons, cubes, cones, cylinders, and spheres).

Standard
K.G.2 Correctly name shapes regardless of their orientations or overall size.

Mathematical Practices

○ Make sense of problems and persevere in solving them.

✔ Reason abstractly and quantitatively.

○ Construct viable arguments and critique the reasoning of others.

○ Model with mathematics.

✔ Use appropriate tools strategically.

○ Attend to precision.

✔ Look for and make use of structure.

○ Look for and express regularity in repeated reasoning.

Problem Solving: Use Objects

 **Lesson Overview**

Objective	Essential Understanding	Vocabulary	Materials
Children will solve problems by using objects.	Some problems can be solved by using objects to act out the actions in the problem.		Pattern blocks (or Teaching Tool 35)

 **PROFESSIONAL DEVELOPMENT**

Math Background

Ask questions to help children understand the relationship between geometric shapes and real-world objects. *Do they both have* *the same shape? How can we tell? Do they both have the same number of sides? How many sides?*

1 Daily Common Core Review

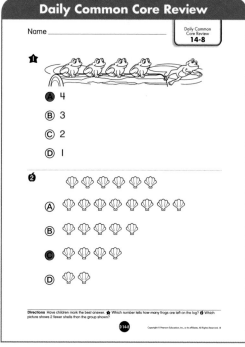

Content Reviewed

Exercise 1   Solve Subtraction Problems

Exercise 2   Identify 2 Fewer

Also available in print

 30 min **Problem-Based Interactive Learning**

Overview Children will learn to solve problems by using objects.

Focus How can you use objects to solve a problem?

Materials (per pair) Pattern Blocks (or Teaching Tool 35)

Set the Purpose Remind children that they have learned about different shapes. *You will learn how to use objects to solve problems about shapes in this lesson.*

Connect Point to objects in your classroom, such as an eraser or a clock. *What shape is the eraser?* [Rectangle] *What shape is the clock?* [Circle]

Repeated Reasoning
Ask children how what they have learned can help them identify shapes and solids they see every day.

Pose the Problem Point to the blue rug on the workmat. *Lin sees a blue rug. She wants to find a pattern block that matches the shape of the rug. How can she solve this problem?* Have children share their ideas before modeling the solution.

Model *What shape is the rug?* [Hexagon] *I want to find the pattern block that matches that shape.* Call on children to hold up the appropriate pattern block. Then have children trace and color the hexagon on the workmat. Point to the green rug on the workmat. *Lin has a green rug in her bedroom. What shape is this rug?* [Square] *Let's find the pattern block that matches that shape.* Have children find the orange square pattern block. Then have them trace and color the square on the workmat.

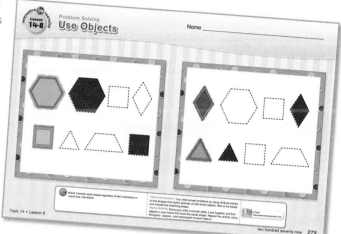

Using Manipulatives Have children place a pattern block on top of the shape to see if it is the same size and same shape. Children can also count the number of sides of the pattern block and the shape to be sure they match.

Small Group Interaction Have partners work together to complete the right side of the page using pattern blocks as you pose these problems: *Which pattern block matches the purple rug?* [Blue pattern block] *Trace and color the shape. Which shape matches the orange rug?* [Triangle] *Trace and color the shape.*

Have children trace pattern blocks to create shapes of other real-world objects.

eTools **Geometry Shapes**
www.pearsonsuccessnet.com

Visual Learning

Read and Understand

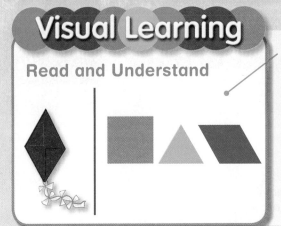

What do you see? [A kite and some pattern blocks] *How can Lin find the block that matches the shape and size of the kite?* Have volunteers share their ideas.

Plan

Lin looks at 3 blocks. What can Lin plan with the blocks? [She can look at the shape and size of each block. She can also count the sides to find a matching block.]

1 Visual Learning

Set the Purpose Call children's attention to the **Visual Learning Bridge** at the top of the page. *In this lesson, you will learn to solve a problem by using blocks to help you match shapes.*

2 Guided Practice

Remind children to look at the size of each shape and to count its sides. Exercise 1 allows children to revisit the Visual Learning Bridge to record how they found a shape to match the real object.

Error Intervention

If children cannot remember which shapes do not match,

then have them mark an X on a shape as it is eliminated.

Do you understand? *How can you find a pattern block that matches the shape of a real object?* [I can look for a block that is the same shape and size as the real object. I can count the number of sides.]

Reteaching In advance, trace the shape of several classroom objects, such as a toy plate, a book, and a musical triangle, on chart paper. Display the objects along with the chart paper. Call on volunteers to match each object to a shape.

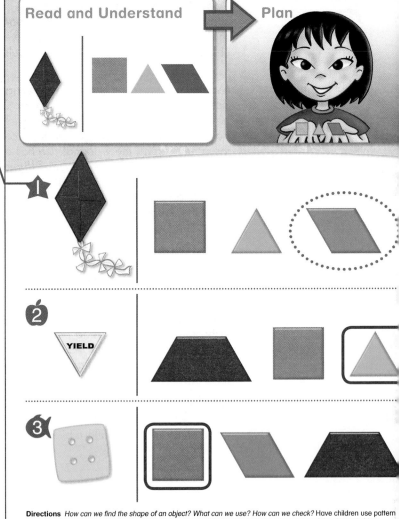

Directions *How can we find the shape of an object? What can we use? How can we check?* Have children use pattern blocks to match the shapes. Then have them circle the pattern block that matches the shape of the pictured object.

Topic 14 • Lesson 8

Solve

How did Lin find the right pattern block?
[The kite has 4 sides. So she crossed out the block with 3 sides. The kite is not a square. So she crossed out the orange block.]

Look Back and Check

How does Lin look back and check? [She thinks about the kite and the block. Both have 4 sides. They are the same shape and size. Lin can put the pattern block on top of the kite to check.]

Solve

Look Back and Check

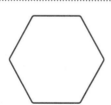

Directions *How can we find the shape of an object? What can we use? How can we check?* Have children find the pattern block that matches the shape of each pictured object, trace the pattern block, and then explain how they know the shapes match.

two hundred eighty   280

Paired Problems

🕐 10-15 min 👥

Materials (per pair) Attribute blocks (or Teaching Tool 36): circle and rectangle; paper, crayons

• Ask partners to look at the 2 blocks and think of real objects that have the same shape as each one, for example: flags, boxes, envelopes (rectangles); plates, cookies, clocks (circles).

• Invite them to make 2 drawings. One should show real objects with the same shape as the circle block. The other should show real objects the same shape as the rectangle block.

• Allow time for partners to share and compare their drawings.

---

3 Independent Practice 🅒 **MATHEMATICAL PRACTICES**

🅒 **Use Appropriate Tools** Children find the pattern block that matches the shape of a pictured object and record by tracing the pattern block. Then they explain their reasoning.

Close

Essential Understanding Some problems can be solved by using objects to act out the actions in the problem. *You can count the sides of each shape. Do they have the same number of sides? You can look at the size. Are they both the same size?*

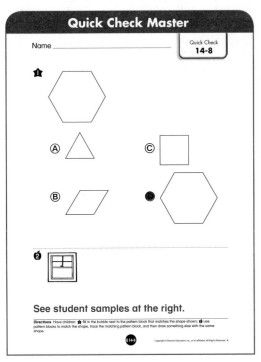

Formative Assessment

Use the **Quick Check** to assess children's understanding.

Ⓒ **ASSESSMENT**

Exercise 1 is worth 1 point.
Use the rubric to score Exercise 2.

Exercise 2
Use Appropriate Tools Children should be able to choose and trace the correct shape, and then draw another object with the same shape.

🅔🅛🅛 **Use Repetition** For children who need additional help, have them repeat descriptions of shapes before beginning their work.

Student Samples
3-point answer Children match the shape, trace the pattern block, and draw another object with the shape of a square.

2-point answer Children match the shape and trace the pattern block but draw an incorrect object.

1-point answer Children incorrectly trace the pattern block or trace an incorrect pattern block.

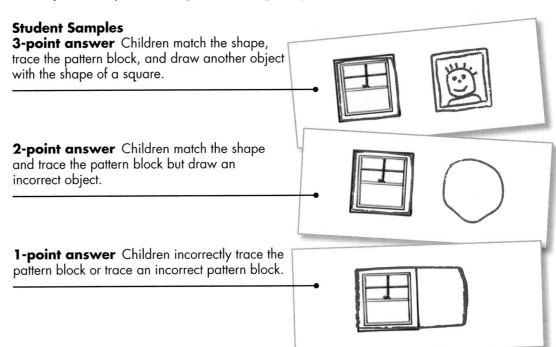

Prescription for Differentiated Instruction
Use children's work on the **Quick Check** to prescribe differentiated instruction.

Points	Prescription
0–2	Intervention
3	On-Level
4	Advanced

Differentiated Instruction

Intervention

Mix and Match Game

 10 min

Materials (per pair) 2 copies of Shapes (Teaching Tool 2): circle, square, rectangle, triangle, hexagon; crayons

- Distribute the cards from Teaching Tool 2.
- Partners place the cards facedown on a table.
- They take turns turning over 2 cards and trying to find matching shapes.
- After all shapes are matched, have them color matching shapes in the same colors.

On-Level

Practice · Center Activity

Helping Hands

Start ↟↟ Get 40 squares.

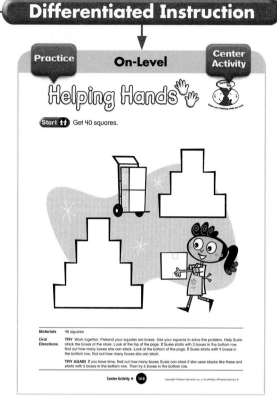

Materials 40 squares

Oral Directions **TRY** Work together. Pretend your squares are boxes. Use your squares to solve the problem. Help Susie stack the boxes of the store. Look at the top of the page. If Susie starts with 3 boxes in the bottom row, find out how many boxes she can stack. Look at the bottom of the page. If Susie starts with 4 boxes in the bottom row, find out how many boxes she can stack.

TRY AGAIN If you have time, find out how many boxes Susie can stack if she uses stacks like these and starts with 5 boxes in the bottom row. Then try 6 boxes in the bottom row.

Center Activity ★ 14-8   Copyright © Pearson Education, Inc., or its affiliates. All Rights Reserved. ★

Advanced

Practice · Center Activity

Helping Hands

Start ↟↟ Get 40 squares.

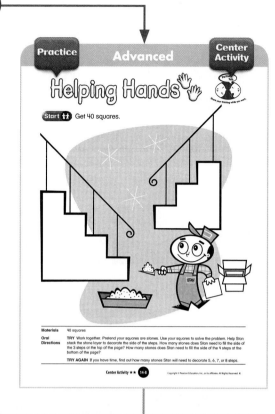

Materials 40 squares

Oral Directions **TRY** Work together. Pretend your squares are stones. Use your squares to solve the problem. Help Stan stack the stone layer to decorate the side of the steps. How many stones does Stan need to fill the side of the 3 steps of the top of the page? How many stones does Stan need to fill the side of the 4 steps of the bottom of the page?

TRY AGAIN If you have time, find out how many stones Stan will need to decorate 5, 6, 7, or 8 steps.

Center Activity ★★ 14-8   Copyright © Pearson Education, Inc., or its affiliates. All Rights Reserved. ★

E L L Report Back Ask a child to repeat and complete this sentence: *A good way to solve the problem about stacking stones is to ___.* [Pretend the squares are stones and use squares to make the pattern; count the squares]

Leveled Homework

Reteaching Master

Name ___   Reteaching 14-8

Problem Solving: Use Objects

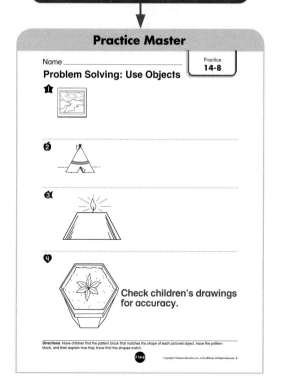

Directions *How can we find the shape of an object? What can we use? How can we check?* Have children use attribute blocks to match the shapes. Then have them color the block that matches the shape of the pictured object.

P 14-8   Copyright © Pearson Education, Inc., or its affiliates. All Rights Reserved. ★

Also available in print

Practice Master

Name ___   Practice 14-8

Problem Solving: Use Objects

Check children's drawings for accuracy.

Directions Have children find the pattern block that matches the shape of each pictured object, trace the pattern block, and then explain how they know that the shapes match.

P 14-8   Copyright © Pearson Education, Inc., or its affiliates. All Rights Reserved. ★

Also available in print

Enrichment Master

Name ___   Enrichment 14-8

Complete the Picture

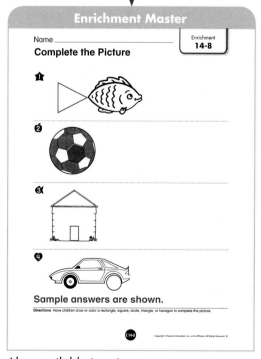

Sample answers are shown.

Directions Have children draw or color a rectangle, square, circle, triangle, or hexagon to complete the picture.

E 14-8   Copyright © Pearson Education, Inc., or its affiliates. All Rights Reserved. ★

Also available in print

MindPoint Quiz Show
Two-Dimensional Shapes
www.pearsonsuccessnet.com

eTools **Geometry Shapes**
www.pearsonsuccessnet.com

Game **Geometry**
www.pearsonsuccessnet.com

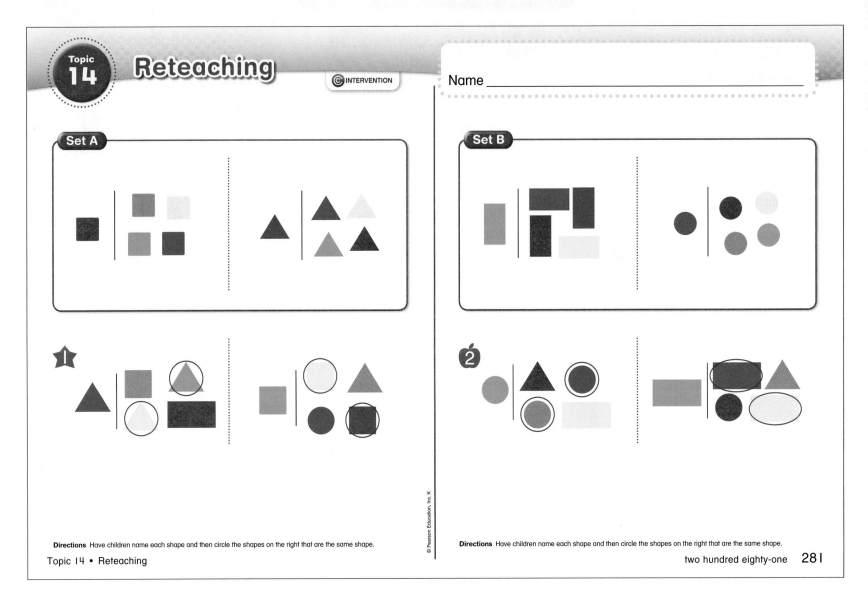

Directions Have children name each shape and then circle the shapes on the right that are the same shape.

Topic 14 • Reteaching

Directions Have children name each shape and then circle the shapes on the right that are the same shape.

two hundred eighty-one   281

Purpose

• Provide children with more examples and practice for each lesson in the topic.

• For intervention materials, use the resources listed in the chart to the right.

Item Analysis for Diagnosis and Intervention

Objective	© Common Core Standards	Reteaching Items	Student Book Lessons	Intervention System
Correctly name shapes regardless of their orientations or overall size.	**K.G.2**	Sets A, B	14-1, 14-2, 14-3, 14-4	D48
Identify shapes as two-dimensional (lying in a plane, "flat") or three-dimensional ("solid").	**K.G.3**	Set C	14-6	D59

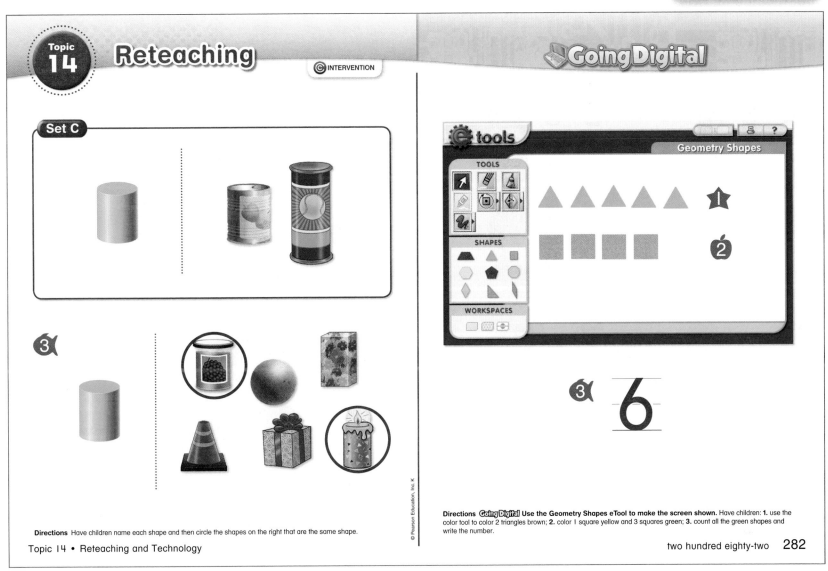

Set C

Directions Have children name each shape and then circle the shapes on the right that are the same shape.

Topic 14 • Reteaching and Technology

© Pearson Education, Inc. K

Directions Going Digital **Use the Geometry Shapes eTool to make the screen shown.** Have children: **1.** use the color tool to color 2 triangles brown; **2.** color 1 square yellow and 3 squares green; **3.** count all the green shapes and write the number.

Response to Intervention

RTI TIER **1** ONGOING

Ongoing Intervention
- Lessons with guiding questions to assess understanding
- Support to prevent misconceptions and to reteach

RTI TIER **2** STRATEGIC

Strategic Intervention
- Targeted to small groups who need more support
- Easy to implement

RTI TIER **3** INTENSIVE

Intensive Intervention
- Instruction to accelerate progress
- Instruction focused on foundational skills

Going Digital

Purpose
- Children will follow directions and identify plane shapes and sort by color to classify.

Count the green triangles. Click 2 of the triangles to color them brown. Count the orange squares. Click one of the squares to color it yellow and the others to color them green. Before children begin to make any changes, challenge them to determine how many triangles will be green after they make the change and how many squares will be green. They can check their answers by clicking over the lightbulb.

Topic 14 Test

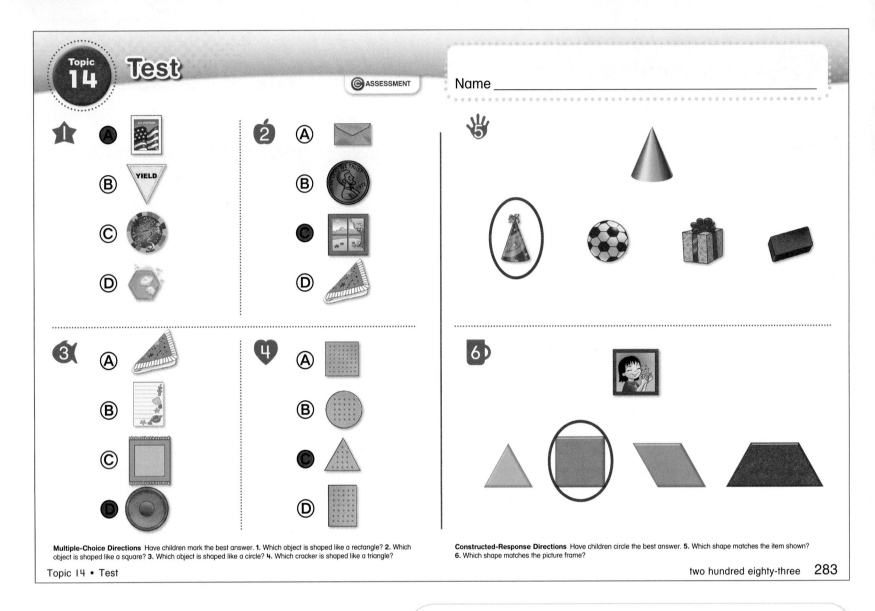

Name _____

Multiple-Choice Directions Have children mark the best answer. **1.** Which object is shaped like a rectangle? **2.** Which object is shaped like a square? **3.** Which object is shaped like a circle? **4.** Which cracker is shaped like a triangle?

Constructed-Response Directions Have children circle the best answer. **5.** Which shape matches the item shown? **6.** Which shape matches the picture frame?

Topic 14 • Test

Purpose

- Assess children's understanding of the concepts and skills in Topic 14 using multiple-choice format.

- Additional assessment options can be found in the Teacher Resource Masters.

- For intervention materials that correspond to all tests, use the resources listed in the chart to the right.

Test-Taking Tips

Discuss with children the following tips for test success.

Understand the Question
- Look for important words.
- Turn the question into a statement: "I need to find out..."

Gather Information
- Get information from text.
- Get information from pictures, tables, and graphs.

Make a Plan
- Think about problem-solving skills and strategies.
- Choose computation methods.

Make Smart Choices
- Eliminate wrong answers.
- Try working backward from an answer.
- Check answers for reasonableness; estimate.

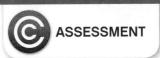

Item Analysis for Diagnosis and Intervention

Objective	Common Core Standards	Test Items	Student Book Lessons	Intervention System
Correctly name shapes regardless of their orientations or overall size.	**K.G.2**	1, 2, 3, 4	14.1, 14.2, 14.3, 14.4	D48
Identify shapes as two-dimensional (lying in a plane, "flat") or three-dimensional ("solid").	**K.G.3**	5, 6	14-6	D48, D49, D50

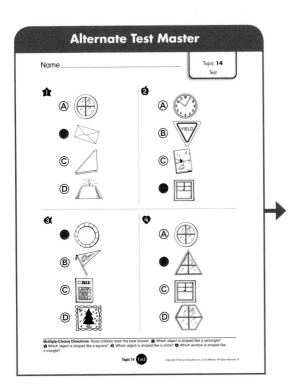

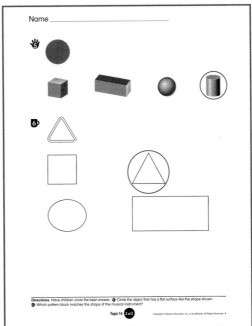

 ASSESSMENT

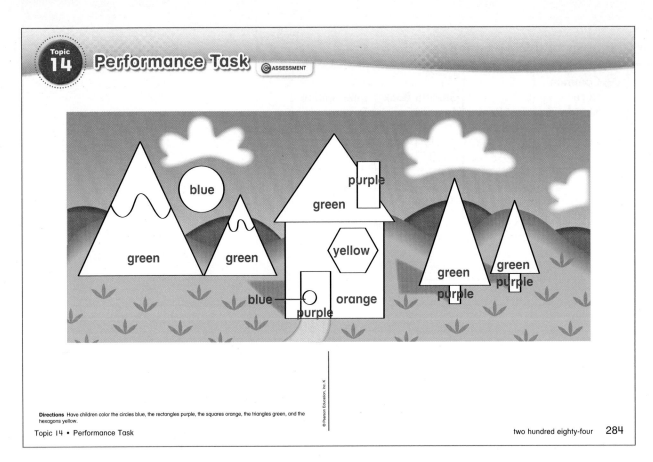

Topic 14 Performance Task _{ASSESSMENT}

Directions Have children color the circles blue, the rectangles purple, the squares orange, the triangles green, and the hexagons yellow.

Topic 14 • Performance Task

© Pearson Education, Inc. K

two hundred eighty-four **284**

Purpose Assess children's understanding of the concepts and skills in Topic 14 through a performance-based task.

Unifying Concept Geometric Figures: Two- and three-dimensional objects with or without curved surfaces can be described, classified, and analyzed by their attributes.

Topic Essential Question How can shapes be named and described?

Task For this assessment, children will identify two-dimensional shapes.

Get Ready Review with the children the attributes of two-dimensional shapes.

Guiding the Activity Explain to children that they are to look at the shapes in the picture. Have them color the objects shaped like circles blue, the objects shaped like rectangles purple, the objects shaped like squares orange, the objects shaped like triangles green, and the objects shaped like hexagons yellow.

Questioning Strategies What shape is the door? What color did you use for the mountains? What color did you use for the window?

Scoring Rubric

Standard to be achieved for performance of specified level

3-point answer The child correctly identifies all two-dimensional shapes.	**2-point answer** The child identifies most of the two-dimensional shapes correctly.	**1-point answer** The child makes an attempt but needs assistance to complete the task.